SPECIAL TOPICS IN TOPOLOGICAL ALGEBRAS

Notes on Mathematics and its Applications

E. Artin, ALGEBRAIC NUMBERS AND ALGEBRAIC FUNCTIONS

R. P. Boas, COLLECTED WORKS OF HIDEHIKO YAMABE

M. Davis, A FIRST COURSE IN FUNCTIONAL ANALYSIS

M. Davis, LECTURES ON MODERN MATHEMATICS

J. Eells, jr., SINGULARITIES OF SMOOTH MAPS

K. O. Friedrichs, ADVANCED ORDINARY DIFFERENTIAL EQUATIONS

K. O. Friedrichs, SPECIAL TOPICS IN FLUID DYNAMICS

K. O. Friedrichs and *H. N. Shapiro*, INTEGRATION IN HILBERT SPACE

A. Guichardet, SPECIAL TOPICS IN TOPOLOGICAL ALGEBRAS

M. Hausner and *J. T. Schwartz*, LIE GROUPS; LIE ALGEBRAS

P. Hilton, HOMOTOPY THEORY AND DUALITY

F. John, LECTURES ON ADVANCED NUMERICAL ANALYSIS

A. M. Krall, STABILITY TECHNIQUES FOR CONTINUOUS LINEAR SYSTEMS

H. Mullish, AN INTRODUCTION TO COMPUTER PROGRAMMING

J. T. Schwartz, W-*ALGEBRAS

J. T. Schwartz, NON-LINEAR FUNCTIONAL ANALYSIS

J. T. Schwartz, DIFFERENTIAL GEOMETRY AND TOPOLOGY

A. Silverman, EXERCISES IN FORTRAN

J. L. Soulé, LINEAR OPERATORS IN HILBERT SPACE

J. J. Stoker, NON-LINEAR ELASTICITY

Additional volumes in preparation

Special topics in topological algebras

A. Guichardet
Professor of the Science Faculty
at the University of Poitiers

GORDON AND BREACH
Science Publishers
New York · London · Paris

Science Publishers, Inc.
150 Fifth Avenue, New York, N. Y. 10011

Library of Congress Catalog Card Number: 67-28242

Editorial Office for Great Britain:

Gordon and Breach Science Publishers Ltd.
8 Bloomsbury Way
London W. C. 1

Editorial Office for France:

Gordon & Breach
7–9 rue Emile Dubois
Paris 14e

Distributed in Canada by:

The Ryerson Press
299 Queen Street West
Toronto 2B, Ontario

Printed in Germany

Editors' Preface

A large number of mathematical books begin as lecture notes; but since mathematicians are busy, and since the labor required to bring lecture notes up to the level of perfection which authors and the public demand of formally published books is very considerable, it follows that an even larger number of lecture notes make the transition to book form only after great delay or not at all. The present lecture note series aims to fill the resulting gap. It will consist of reprinted lecture notes, edited at least to a satisfactory level of completeness and intelligibility, though not necessarily to the perfection which is expected of a book. In addition to lecture notes, the series will include volumes of collected reprints of journal articles as current developments indicate, and mixed volumes including both notes and reprints.

JACOB T. SCHWARTZ
MAURICE LÉVY

Contents

Commutative Banach algebras

Von Neumann Algebras

Topological algebras and holomorphic functions

COMMUTATIVE BANACH ALGEBRAS

CONTENTS

INTRODUCTION

The theory of commutative Banach algebras, due mainly to Russian mathematicians such as G. E. Šilov, I. M. Gelfand, M. A. Naïmark, D. A. Raïkov, is considered as one of the most beautiful applications of the theory of Banach spaces; its original object was to set in a more general frame the results of harmonic analysis, itself a generalization to commutative locally compact groups of the theory of Fourier transformation on the group of real numbers; we will describe here the theory of commutative Banach algebras for its own sake, leaving till a later seminar (*Analyse harmonique commutative*, Dunod; to appear), because of its importance, the application to Harmonic Analysis; we will consider the latter only in the case of the group of integers, in other words of Fourier *series*, which will nevertheless allow us to prove as an application a theorem of Wiener (§§ 1.1 and 1.5, example (*f*)).

The characteristic feature of commutative Banach algebras, that which distinguishes them from the commutative algebras usually studied in Algebra, is the fact that the quotient of a commutative Banach algebra with unit by a maximal ideal is always isomorphic to the field of complex numbers (cf. Corollary 1.5); this explains why maximal ideals take precedence here over prime ideals, and allows us to represent the elements of our algebra as *functions* (Gelfand transformation, § 2.2); we realize thus that functions are going to play an important role in the theory; in fact they will be essentially, on the one hand, functions of one or several complex variables, of which we will use some relatively classical properties (§ 1.4, chaptes III and IV), and on the other, continuous functions on compact or locally compact spaces (§§ 2.2 and 7.3); in return, the theory we will describe will allow us to find once more some known results concerning functions of several complex variables (Theorem 4.2 and § 6.3, no. 6); but we must add that as regards these functions, we will soon find it necessary to use topological algebras which are not Banach.

Knowledge of the following is required in order to understand this paper: algebraic concepts recalled in Chapter 0; topological concepts referring mostly to compact spaces; the elementary theory of functions of one or several complex variables with value in a Banach space, as it is described in the book on analysis by J. Dieudonné; some properties of differential forms with values in a Banach space, Stokes' formula among others; finally a few theorems concerning Banach spaces (closed-graph theorem and Krein-Milnan theorem). We systematically restricted ourselves to commutative algebras, even when this restriction was not necessary, in order to avoid changing hypotheses too frequently; however we will now indicate the main results which remain true for arbitrary Banach algebras: Theorems 1.1 and 1.2, Corollary 1.5, Proposition 1.1 (but not Theorem 1.3!), Theorem 3.1, Propositions 7.1, 7.2, 7.3, 7.5; Theorem 4.1 can be generalized if we assume that the elements $a_1, \ldots, a_n$ commute.

In the last chapter we describe, as applications, the theory of compactifications of completely regular topological spaces and the spectral theory of normal operators in Hilbert spaces.

CHAPTER 0

ALGEBRAIC PRELIMINARIES

§ 0.1. *Generalities*

We will only be dealing with *commutative algebras over the field* $\mathfrak{C}$ *of complex numbers*; for the concepts of algebra, subalgebra, ideal, quotient, see reference [3]; the unit element, if it exists, will be denoted by e. We will call *morphism* of an algebra A into algebra B any mapping from A into B which transforms sums into sums, products into products, and products by a scalar k into products by k. A subalgebra B of an algebra A with unit (also called *unitary*) will be said to be *full* if any element of B invertible in A is invertible in B.

The subalgebra generated by a family of elements $(x_1, \ldots, x_n)$ is the set of elements of the form $P(x_1, \ldots, x_n)$, where P is a polynomial with complex coefficients without constant term; the full subalgebra generated by the same family is the set of elements $P(x_1, \ldots, x_n)$ $(Q(x_1, \ldots, x_n))^{-1}$.

When the word "ideal" will be used, "distinct from A" will nearly always be understood; if A is unitary, any ideal is contained in at least one maximal ideal (theorem of Krull); in order that an element be invertible it is necessary and sufficient that it belong to no maximal ideal.

§ 0.2. *Adjunction of a unit*

The non-unitary case can be reduced to the unitary case by a standard operation called the *adjunction of a unit* (actually it is possible even when the original algebra A is unitary); we endow the set $\tilde{A} = A \times C$ with the operations

$$(x, \lambda) + (y, \mu) = (x + y, \lambda + \mu)$$

$$\alpha(x, \lambda) = (\alpha x, \alpha\lambda)$$

$$(x, \lambda) \quad (y, \mu) = (xy + \lambda y + \mu x, \lambda\mu)$$

which transform it into an algebra with a unit element $e = (0,1)$; we identify A with the maximal ideal of $\tilde{A}$ composed of the elements $(x, 0)$ and we often write $x + \lambda e$ instead of (x, λ).

§ 0.3. *Regular ideals*

See reference [4], Appendix. An ideal I of an algebra A is called *regular* (sometimes "modular") if the algebra A/I is unitary, i.e. if there is an element u of A satisfying $ux - x \in I$ for all $x \in A$; such an element is called a *unit modulo* I; if A is unitary, all ideals are regular. If u is a unit modulo I, we have $u \notin I$; any ideal containing a regular ideal is regular; applying Zorn's theorem we see that any regular ideal is contained in at least one maximal regular ideal; such an ideal is always a maximal ideal and the quotient is a field. The regular ideals (resp. maximal regular ideals) of A are exactly the traces on A of the ideals (resp. maximal ideals) of $\tilde{A}$ which are not contained in A; the correspondence is bijective for maximal ideals.

The *radical* of A (sometimes called "Jacobson radical") is the intersection of the maximal regular ideals; it will be denoted rad A; it contains the set of nilpotent elements (and is equal to it if A has finite dimension); A is said to *have no radical* if rad $A = \{0\}$; (if A is finite-dimensional, this is equivalent to saying that A is semi-simple); $A/\text{rad}\, A$ is always without radical.

§ 0.4. *Spectrum of an element*

In this section and the following we will give definitions which are not adopted for all topological algebras; however they do not seem out of place in these "algebraic preliminaries".

If A is a unitary algebra, the *spectrum* of an element x of A, denoted $\text{sp}_A\, x$ or more simply sp x, is the set of complex numbers λ for which $x - \lambda e$ is non-invertible; if B is a subalgebra of A containing e and x, we obviously have $\text{sp}_B\, x \supset \text{sp}_A\, x$; if B is full we have equality.

We will call *resolvent* of x the mapping $\lambda \to R(x, \lambda) = (x - \lambda e)^{-1}$ of $\mathfrak{C} - \text{sp}\, x$ into A; it satisfies the fundamental identity.

$$R(x, \lambda_1) - R(x, \lambda_0) = (\lambda_1 - \lambda_0)\, R(x, \lambda_1)\, R(x, \lambda_0). \tag{1}$$

If A is a non-unitary algebra we set by definition $\text{sp}_A\, x = \text{sp}_{\tilde{A}}\, x$; then $\text{sp}_A\, x$ always contains 0; to say that a non-zero number λ does not belong to $\mathrm{sp}_A\, x$ amounts to saying that there is a $y \in A$ satisfying $\frac{x}{\lambda} y - \frac{x}{\lambda} - y = 0$; $\Big($such a y is sometimes called "adverse" or "quasi-inverse" of $\frac{x}{\lambda}\Big)$.

§ 0.5. *Characters*

We call *character* of an algebra A any non-zero morphism of A into $\mathfrak{C}$; a character is always surjective; its kernel is a regular maximal ideal; two characters with the same kernel are identical; if A is unitary we have $\chi(e) = 1$ for any character χ. We call *spectrum* of A and denote by $\hat{A}$ the set of characters of A.

Let I be an ideal of A; two characters which have the same non-zero restriction to I are identical; any character of I extends uniquely into a character of A (this will be proved in Proposition 2.5). Let ω be the character of $\tilde{A}$ which is zero on A ($\omega(x + \lambda e) = \lambda$); the mapping $\chi \to \chi|A$ is a bijection of $\hat{\tilde{A}} - \{\omega\}$ onto $\hat{A}$ thanks to which we often identify $\hat{A}$ with a subset of $\hat{\tilde{A}}$.

§ 0.6. *Involutive algebras* (or *with involution* or **-algebras*)

An *involution* on an algebra A is a mapping of A onto A, denoted $x \to x^*$, satisfying the following axioms;

$$(\lambda x + \mu y)^* = \bar{\lambda} x^* + \bar{\mu} y^*$$
$$(xy)^* = y^* x^*$$
$$x^{**} = x$$

x^* is called the *adjoint* of x.

If A is unitary we necessarily have $e^* = e$; if x has an inverse, so does x^* and $(x^*)^{-1} = (x^{-1})^*$; $\mathrm{sp}\, x^*$ is the conjugate set of $\mathrm{sp}\, x$.

An element x is *hermitian* if it is equal to its adjoint; the hermitian elements form a real subalgebra A_h of A; the elements of form xx^* are called *positive*; they are obviously hermitian; we note that in general they do not form a convex cone. Any element x can be written uniquely in the form $x = x_1 + ix_2$ where x_1 and x_2 are hermitian. An element x of an algebra with identity is said to be *unitary* if $xx^* = e$; the unitary elements form a subgroup of the multiplicative group of invertible elements.

If A is an involutive algebra, the algebra $\tilde{A}$ becomes an involutive algebra if we set $(x + \lambda e)^* = x^* + \bar{\lambda} e$.

For any subset E of an involutive algebra A we denote by E^* the set of x^* where x runs over E; E is said to be *selfadjoint* if $E^* = E$. The self-adjoint subalgebra generated by a family $(x_1, \ldots, x_n)$ is the set of elements of the form $P(x_1, \ldots, x_n, x_1^*, \ldots, x_n^*)$, where P is a polynomial without constant term.

If I is a self-adjoint ideal, A/I is an involutive algebra if we set $(\dot{x})^* = (x^*)^\bullet$; a morphism of involutive algebras $A \to B$ is a morphism of algebras transforming adjoint into adjoint; its kernel is a self-adjoint ideal; conversely, if I is a self-adjoint ideal, the canonical mapping $A \to A/I$ is a morphism of involutive algebras.

A regular maximal ideal is not necessarily self-adjoint; the mapping $I \to I^*$ is a bijection of the set of regular maximal ideals into itself; it follows that the radical is self-adjoint.

§ 0.7. *Positive linear forms*

The form f^* defined by $f^*(x) = \overline{f(x^*)}$ is called the *adjoint* of a linear form f on A; the adjoint of a character is a character; f is said to be *hermitian* if $f^* = f$; this happens if and only if the restriction of f to A_h is real; there is a bijective correspondence between the hermitian forms on A and the linear (real) forms on A_h. Any linear form on A can be expressed uniquely in the form $f_1 + if_2$, where f_1 and f_2 are hermitian.

A linear form on A is said to be *positive* if it assumes positive values on the set of positive elements; the positive forms form a convex cone; if A is unitary, any positive form is hermitian; in general we can only assert that $f(x^*y^*) = \overline{f(xy)}$. A character is positive if and only if it is hermitian.

All positive forms satisfy the *Schwarz inequality*

$$|f(xy)|^2 \leqq f(xx^*)\, f(yy^*);$$

if f is a positive hermitian form on A, there does not always exist a positive form $\tilde{f}$ on $\tilde{A}$ extending f; it will exist if and only if f satisfies an inequality of the form

$$|f(x)|^2 \leqq k f(xx^*)$$

and in this case we can take $\tilde{f}(x + \lambda e) = f(x) + k\lambda$; f will then be said to be *extendable*.

CHAPTER I

GENERALITIES, SPECTRA, CHARACTERS

The sections 1.6 and 1.7 can be omitted on first reading.

§ 1.1. *Definitions*

We call a *commutative Banach algebra* (abbreviated to C. B. A.) any commutative algebra over $\mathfrak{C}$ endowed with a norm and complete for the associated uniform structure, where a norm is a mapping $x \to \|x\|$ of A into R_+ satisfying

$$\|x\| = 0 \quad \text{if and only if } x = 0$$

$$\|x + y\| \leqq \|x\| + \|y\|$$

$$\|\lambda x\| = |\lambda| \, \|x\|$$

$$\|xy\| \leqq \|x\| \, \|y\|;$$

if A admits a unit e we will always assume $\|e\| = 1$. Then $\widetilde{A}$ is also a C. B. A. for the norm

$$\|x + \lambda e\| = \|x\| + |\lambda|.$$

§ 1.2. *Examples*

In the examples (a) to (d) we are dealing with algebras of complex, functions bounded on a certain set X, where the operations of addition, multiplication and multiplication by a scalar are the usual operations and the norm is that of uniform convergence: $\|f\| = \sup_{x \in X} |f(x)|$; in the examples (e) and (f) we still have algebras of functions with the usual operations, but the norm is different.

(a) The algebra $\mathscr{C}^\infty(X)$ of the continuous functions bounded on a topological space X.

(b) (*A particular case of the preceding example*) The algebra $\mathscr{C}(X)$ of the continuous functions on a compact space X.

(c) The algebra $\mathscr{C}_0(X)$ of the functions which are continuous and zero at infinity on a locally compact space X; if X is compact we have again the preceding example; otherwise $\mathscr{C}_0(X)$ admits no unit element; the algebra obtained by adjunction of a unit is algebraically isomorphic to $\mathscr{C}(X')$ (X' = the Alexandrov compactification of X).

(d) The algebra of the complex functions continuous on the closed disc $\Delta : |z| \leqq 1$, and holomorphic in its interior.

(e) The algebra $\mathscr{D}^m_{[0,1]}$ of the complex functions m times continuously differentiable on $[0, 1]$ with the norm

$$\|f\| = \sum_{p=0}^{m} \frac{1}{p!} \sup |f^{(p)}(x)|.$$

Note that the algebra of the indefinitely differentiable functions on $[0, 1]$ admits no norm which makes it into a Banach algebra (cf. § 2.3, exercise 2).

(f) The algebra of the complex functions on the torus $\mathbb{T}$, which can be expanded in absolutely convergent Fourier series, namely $f(t) = \sum_{-\infty}^{+\infty} c_n e^{int}$, with the norm $\|f\| = \sum_{-\infty}^{+\infty} |c_n|$. We can also consider this algebra as the set of complex sequences $c = (c_n)_{n \in Z}$ satisfying $\sum_{-\infty}^{+\infty} |c_n| < +\infty$, where addition and multiplication are defined in the obvious manner and multiplication by

$$(cc')_n = \sum_{p=-\infty}^{+\infty} c_{n-p} c'_p$$

(convolution product).

This algebra is a particular case of the group algebras $L^1(G)$ and $M^1(G)$ which lie at the foundations of Harmonic Analysis.

(g) The algebra $L^\infty(X, \mu)$ of the classes of measurable functions which are essentially bounded for a positive measure μ on a space X. with the norm

$$\|f\| = \sup \operatorname{ess} |f(x)|.$$

(h) Any commutative closed subalgebra of the Banach algebra $\mathscr{L}(H)$ (in general it is not commutative) of the continuous linear operators in a complex Banach space H.

(i) The Banach space $L^1([0, 1])$ where the product is defined by

$$(fg)(x) = \int_0^x f(x - y)\, g(y)\, dy;$$

it admits no unit element.

(j) The space $\mathfrak{C}^2$ where the product is defined by

$$(a, b)\,(a', b') = (aa', ab' + ba').$$

§ 1.3. *Invertible elements*

Theorem 1.1. The set of invertible elements in a commutative Banach algebra with unit is open and contains the open ball with centre e and radius 1; moreover the mapping $x \to x^{-1}$ is continuous on this set.

If $\|x\| < 1$, the series $\sum_0^\infty x^n$ is absolutely convergent, hence convergent, and its sum trivially satisfies $(e - x) \sum_0^\infty x_n = e$, whence the second assertion. To prove the first, let us suppose that x is invertible; then for $\|y\| < \|x^{-1}\|^{-1}$ we have $\|x^{-1}y\| < 1$, hence $e + x^{-1}y$ is invertible and so is $x + y = x(e + x^{-1}y)$. Finally, still supposing $\|y\| < \|x^{-1}\|^{-1}$, we have

$$(x + y)^{-1} - x^{-1} = x^{-1}\left((e + x^{-1}y)^{-1} - e\right) = x^{-2}y \sum_0^\infty (x^{-1}y)^n\,(-1)^{n+1}$$

$$\|(x + y)^{-1} - x^{-1}\| \leqq \|x^{-2}\|\, \|y\| \,/\, (1 - \|x^{-1}\|\, \|y\|)$$

whence the announced continuity.

Corollary 1.1. The set of invertible elements is a topological group for the operation of multiplication and for the induced topology.

Corollary 1.2. All maximal ideals of a C. B. A. with unit are closed.

Indeed, for any ideal I, $\bar{I}$ is distinct from A since we have $\|x - e\| \geqq 1$ for all $x \in I$ and hence for all $x \in \bar{I}$; $\bar{I}$ is hence an ideal, and if I is maximal we have $I = \bar{I}$.

Corollary 1.3. All regular maximal ideals of a C. B. A. are closed. Follows from § 0.3.

Remark. It can be proved that the quotient of the group of invertible elements by the connected component of e is isomorphic to the first cohomology group $H^1(A, \mathfrak{Z})$ (cf. [35]).

§ 1.4. *Spectrum of an element*

Theorem 1.2. The spectrum of an arbitrary element x in a commutative Banach algebra with unit is compact, contained in the disc $|z| \leqq \|x\|$ and non-empty; the resolvent is holomorphic at each point of $\mathfrak{C} - \operatorname{sp} x$ as well as at infinity.

The spectrum of x is the inverse image of the closed set of non-invertible elements of A under the continuous mapping $\lambda \to x - \lambda e$, it is hence closed; it is contained in the disc in question since, if $|\lambda| > \|x\|$, $\frac{x}{y} - e$ is invertible and the same holds for $x - \lambda e$.

The holomorphy of the resolvent at each point of $\mathfrak{C} - \operatorname{sp} x$ follows from its continuity and from the identity (1) of § 0.4.; for the point at infinity, it suffices to note that

$$\lim_{\mu \to 0} \frac{1}{\mu} R\left(x, \frac{1}{\mu}\right) = \lim_{\mu \to 0} (\mu x - e)^{-1} = -e.$$

Finally if $\operatorname{sp} x$ were empty, the resolvent would be holomorphic at all points of $\mathfrak{C}$ including the point at infinity, hence constant by virtue of the Liouville theorem, that is $(x - \lambda e)\, y = e$ for all λ; in particular $xy = e$, whence $\lambda y = 0$ for all λ, which is absurd.

Corollary 1.4. In a C. B. A. the spectrum of an element is compact and non-empty.

Corollary 1.5. (Gelfand-Mazur). Any C. B. A with unit which is a field is isomorphic to $\mathfrak{C}$.

Indeed, for all $x \in A$ there is a λ such that $x - \lambda e$ is non-invertible; then $x = \lambda e$.

Definition. The number $\sup |\lambda|$ for $\lambda \in \operatorname{sp} x$ is called the *spectral radius* of x and is denoted by $\nu(x)$.

We always have $\nu(x) \leqq \|x\|$; we will see later (Theorem 2.2) that ν is a semi-norm.

Proposition 1.1. We have

$$\nu(x) = \lim_{n \to \infty} \|x^n\|^{1/n} = \inf_n \|x^n\|^{1/n}.$$

We can assume A is unitary; if $\lambda \in \operatorname{sp} x$ we have $\lambda^n \in \operatorname{sp} x^n$ since

$$x^n - \lambda^n e = (x - \lambda e) \sum_{p=0}^{n-1} x^p \lambda^{n-p-1};$$

hence

$$|\lambda|^n \leqq \|x^n\|,\ |\lambda| \leqq \|x^n\|^{1/n} \quad \text{and} \quad \nu(x) \leqq \inf_n \|x^n\|^{1/n} \leqq \underline{\lim}\, \|x^n\|^{1/n}.$$

On the other hand, since the mapping $\mu \to (x - \mu e)^{-1}$ is holomorphic at each point such that $|\mu| > \nu(x)$ as well as at the point at infinity, the mapping $\lambda \to \left(x - \frac{e}{\lambda}\right)^{-1}$ is holomorphic at each point such that $|\lambda| < 1/\nu(x)$ and the same is true for $\lambda \to -\frac{1}{\lambda}\left(x - \frac{e}{\lambda}\right)^{-1} = (e - \lambda x)^{-1}$; but for λ sufficiently small, $(e - \lambda x)^{-1} = \sum_0^\infty \lambda^n x^n$; the radius of convergence of this series, equal to $1/\overline{\lim}\, \|x^n\|^{1/n}$, is hence at least equal to $1/\nu(x)$, i.e. $\nu(x) \geqq \overline{\lim}\, \|x^n\|^{1/n}$; whence the proposition.

Corollary 1.6. The spectral radius $\nu(x)$, contrarily to the spectrum sp x, does not depend on the ambient algebra.

Remark. In [15] 5.8, one will find a more detailed study of the resolvent and, more generally, of the solutions of (1).

Exercise. Another proof of $\lim \|x^n\|^{1/n} = \inf \|x^n\|^{1/n}$. (Take $m = nq + r$ with $0 \leqq r < n$ and show that $\|x^m\|^{1/m}$ is majorized by $\|x^n\|^{1/n}$ multiplied by a term which tends to 1; note that this result compares with a property of subadditive functions (cf. § 8.2, no. 4)).

§ 1.5. *Characters*

Theorem 1.3. Let A be a commutative Banach algebra; by associating its kernel to each character of A we obtain a bijective correspondence between the spectrum $\hat{A}$ of A and the set of regular maximal ideals of A.

We know (cf. § 0.5) that the kernel of a character is a regular maximal ideal and that two distinct characters have distinct kernels; let now I be a regular maximal ideal; A/I is a unitary C. B. A. without non-zero ideals, hence a field, hence it is algebraically isomorphic to the field of complex numbers.

Corollary 1.7. All unitary C. B. A. admit at least one character.

Proposition 1.2. Let x be an element of A, and E be the set of numbers $\chi(x)$, $\chi \in \hat{A}$; we have sp $x = E \cup \{0\}$ if A is non-unitary, and sp $x = E$ if A is unitary.

Let us first suppose A is unitary; to say that a number λ belongs to sp x amounts to saying that $x - \lambda e$ belongs to at least one maximal ideal, hence that $\chi(x) = \lambda$ for at least one character χ. Now if A is non-unitary, sp x = $\text{sp}_{\tilde{A}}\, x$ = the set of numbers $\chi(x)$ for $\chi \in \hat{\tilde{A}}$, but $\hat{\tilde{A}}$ is the union of $\hat{A}$ and of the character of $\tilde{A}$ which is zero on A.

Corollary 1.8. Any character of a C. B. A. A is continuous and has norm $\leqq 1$; it has norm 1 if A is unitary.

Indeed, for all x and all χ we have: $|\chi(x)| \leqq \nu(x) \leqq \|x\|$; if A is unitary $\|\chi\| = 1$ since $\chi(e) = 1$.

Corollary 1.9. If $x \in A$ and if P is a polynomial with complex coefficients, we have sp $P(x) = P(\text{sp } x)$.

Spectra of the examples

(a) See § 8.1; let us say immediately that the spectrum contains the characters $f \to f(x)$ where $x \in X$ as well as many others.

(c) We will show that any closed ideal of $\mathscr{C}_0(X)$ is the set of functions which are zero on a certain closed subset of X; it will also be clear that *the characters will be in bijective correspondence with the points of X, the character $f \to f(x)$ corresponding to each point x*. Let thus I be a closed ideal of $\mathscr{C}_0(X)$; let F be the set of x for which all the functions of I are equal to zero; we will see that any function $f \in \mathscr{C}_0(X)$, zero on F, is a uniform limit of elements of I, hence belongs to I. Let $\varepsilon > 0$; the set Y of x such that $|f(x)| \geqq \varepsilon$ is compact and contained in $X - F$; for any $x \in Y$ there is a $g_x \in I$ such that $g_x(x) \neq 0$; g_x is $\neq 0$ in an open neighbourhood V_x of x; let $x_1, \ldots, x_n$ be such that $V_{x_1}, \ldots, V_{x_n}$ cover Y; $g = \sum_1^n g_{x_i}\bar{g}_{x_i}$ belongs to I and is > 0 on Y; there exists thus a $g' \in I$, $g' \geqq 0$ and $g'(x) \geqq \varepsilon$ for all $x \in Y$; let $g'' = \sup(g', \varepsilon)$; we have $fg'/g'' \in I$ and we can readily verify that $\|f - fg'/g''\| \leqq \varepsilon$.

(b) This is a particular case of the previous one.

(d) Let us first show that any function of the algebra A in question is a uniform limit of polynomials; let $f \in A$; for all $\varepsilon > 0$ let us set $f_\varepsilon(z) = f(z(1 - \varepsilon))$; f_ε is holomorphic for $|z| < 1/(1 - \varepsilon)$, hence the limit of polynomials uniformly on Δ; then f is the uniform limit of the f_ε. This being so, A is the closed subalgebra generated by the function $z \to z$, whose spectrum is Δ; the mapping $\chi \to \chi\,(z \to z)$ is hence a bijection of $\hat{A}$ onto Δ; finally to each point x of Δ there corresponds the character $f \to f(x)$ (it is easy to see this is so when f is a polynomial, and the general case follows by continuity); finally *the result is the same as that of example* (c).

(e) Let I be a maximal ideal of $D^m_{[0,1]}$; the functions of I are simultaneously equal to zero at at least one point x_0, because otherwise we could construct as in (c) a function of I which is strictly positive, hence invertible; I is hence contained in the ideal composed of the f which are zero at x_0, and hence equal to it; once more we find *the same result as in* (c).

(f) The algebra in question is the full closed subalgebra generated by the function $f_0 : t \to e^{it}$; on the other hand $\operatorname{sp} f_0 = \mathsf{U}$ (the set of complex numbers of modulus 1); indeed $\operatorname{sp} f_0$ obviously contains U; conversely, if $\lambda \in \operatorname{sp} f_0$ we have $|\lambda| \leqq 1$ since $\|f_0\| = 1$; and $\left|\frac{1}{\lambda}\right| \leqq 1$ since $\frac{1}{\lambda} \in \operatorname{sp} \frac{1}{f_0}$ and $\left\|\frac{1}{f_0}\right\| = 1$.
Whence we see that *the result is again the same as in* (c). From this we readily deduce a *theorem of Wiener*; if a complex function f on $\mathbb{T}$ can be expanded in an absolutely convergent Fourier series and is nowhere equal to zero, $\frac{1}{f}$ can also be expanded in an absolutely convergent Fourier series.

(g) We will consider this case in § 8.3.

(i) $L^1([0, 1])$ is the closed subalgebra generated by the function $f_0 : t \to 1$ since $f_0^n(t) = t^{n-1}/(n-1)!$; on the other hand

$$\nu(f_0) = \lim \|f_0^n\|^{1/n} = \lim (n!)^{-1/n} = 0;$$

hence the algebra we are considering *does not admit any characters*.

(j) We readily verify that the only character is $(a, b) \to a$.

Exercise. The set of elements of A whose spectrum is contained in a given open subset U of $\mathfrak{C}$ is open.

(Let x be such that $\operatorname{sp} x \subset U$ and let d be the distance from $\operatorname{sp} x$ to $\mathfrak{C} - U$; show that $\nu(y - x) < d \Rightarrow \operatorname{sp} y \subset U$.]

§ 1.6. *Topological divisors of zero*

Definition. An element x of a C. B. A. A is called a *topological divisor of zero* if there is a sequence of elements y_n of A satisfying $\|y_n\| \geqq 1$ and $xy_n \to 0$.

Any divisor of zero is a topological divisor of zero and topological divisors of zero are non-invertible.

Proposition 1.3. Any non-invertible element x (of *a* unitary C. B. A.), limit of sequence of invertible elements x_n, is a topological divisor of zero.

First $\|x_n^{-1}\|$ is not bounded; because if we had $\|x_n^{-1}\| \leqq k$ for all n we would have

$$\|x_m^{-1} - x_n^{-1}\| = \|x_m^{-1}(x_n - x_m)\, x_n^{-1}\| \leqq k^2\, \|x_n - x_m\| \to 0$$

hence x_n^{-1} would have a limit y; then

$$xy = (x - x_n)\, y + (y - x_n^{-1})\, x_n + e \to e$$

$$xy = e$$

whence a contradiction. Taking a subsequence we can suppose $\|x_n^{-1}\| \to +\infty$; let us set $y_n = x_n^{-1}/\|x_n^{-1}\|$; we have $\|y_n\| = 1$ and

$$xy_n = (x - x_n)\, y_n + e \,/\, \|x_n^{-1}\| \to 0.$$

Q. E. D.

In particular if λ belongs to the boundary of the spectrum of an element x, $x - \lambda e$ is a topological divisor of zero; it follows that $x - \lambda e$ cannot be invertible in any unitary Banach algebra, commutative or not, containing A; one sometines says that λ is a "permanent spectral singularity of x".

Exercises

1. In example (b) the topological divisors of zero are the functions which equal zero at least once (in other words, the non-invertible elements). In example (c) with X non-compact, all elements are topological divisors of zero.

2. Let H be a complex Banach space; in order that an element x of $\mathscr{L}(H)$ be non-invertible, it is necessary and sufficient that there exist a sequence $y_n \in \mathscr{L}(H)$ such that $\|y_n\| \geqq 1$ and that xy_n or $y_n x \to 0$.

3. Let $A \subset B$ be two C. B. A. with the same unit element e; if $x \in A$ and if $\mathrm{sp}_B\, x$ is real, then $\mathrm{sp}_A\, x = \mathrm{sp}_B\, x$.

§ 1.7. *Approximate units*

Definition. We call an *approximate unit* of a C. B. A. A any family (e_i) of elements of A, indexed by an ordered set I filtering to the right, and satisfying

$$\|e_i\| \leqq 1 \quad \text{and} \quad e_i x - x \to 0 \quad \text{for all} \quad x \in A.$$

In some cases approximate units can replace the units . . . which are obviously particular cases of them (for instance Chapter VII); it must not be thought that e_i tends to the unit of $\tilde{A}$, for the simple reason that A is a closed subset of $\tilde{A}$; however this can happen in a certain sense (cf. § 7.1, exercise).

Examples

(c) The compact subsets of X form a right-filtering set for the relation $\subset$; we obtain an approximate unit of $\mathscr{C}_0(X)$ by taking, for each compact subset K, a function $f_K \in \mathscr{C}_0(X)$, equal to 1 on K and with norm 1.

(i) The open neighbourhoods of 0 in $[0, 1]$ form a right-filtering set for the relation $\supset$; we obtain an approximate unit of $L^1([0, 1])$ by taking for each open neighbourhood V a positive function f_V, zero outside V and with integral 1.

In Chapter VII we will use the

Proposition 1.4. Let A be a C. B. A. with approximate unit; for any sequence x_n tending to zero there exist an element y and a sequence z_n tending to zero, which satisfy $x_n = yz_n$.

Of which there is a proof in [38].

Corollary 1.10. Any element of A is the product of two elements of A.

CHAPTER II

THE SPECTRUM AND GELFAND TRANSFORMATION

§ 2.1. *Topology of the spectrum*

Let first A be a C. B. A. with unit; a character of A, being continuous and of norm 1, is an element of the unit ball of the topological dual vector space A' of A; on the other hand the set $\hat{A}$ of the characters is weakly closed in A' since the characters are characterized by the conditions

$$\chi(e) = 1, \ \chi(xy) = \chi(x) \cdot \chi(y) \qquad \forall\, x, y \in A;$$

hence if we endow $\hat{A}$ with the topology induced by the weak topology of A', we obtain a compact space.

Now if A has no unit, the characters of A are exactly the restrictions of the characters of $\tilde{A}$, with the exception of the character ω zero on A, and it is clear, from the formula $\chi\,(x + e) = \chi(x) + \lambda$, that the mapping $\chi \to \chi/A$ of $\hat{\tilde{A}} - \{\omega\}$ onto A is a homeomorphism for the weak topologies; $\tilde{A}$ is hence a locally compact space whose Alexandrov compactification is homeomorphic to $\hat{\tilde{A}}$. In short

Theorem 2.1. The spectrum $\hat{A}$ of a commutative Banach algebra A, endowed with the topology of simple convergence, is a locally compact space, compact if A admits a unit; $\hat{\tilde{A}}$ is homeomorphic to the Alexandrov compactification of $\hat{A}$, the point at infinity corresponding to the character ω of $\tilde{A}$ which is zero on A.

This result will be made more precise by Theorem 4.3. Note that the topology of $\hat{A}$, like $\hat{A}$ itself, is independent of the topology chosen on A; they are attributes of the "banachizable" algebra A rather than of the Banach algebra A.

Proposition 2.1. If A (assumed to be unitary) is the full closed subalgebra generated by x and e, the mapping $\chi \to \chi(x)$ of $\hat{A}$ onto sp x is a homeomorphism.

Because it is bijective and continuous and $\hat{A}$ is compact.

Remark 2.1. If A is separable, $\hat{A}$ is metrizable.

Examples. We have seen that for each of the examples (b), (c), (d), (e), (f) the spectrum is in bijective correspondence with the set on which the functions are defined; these correspondences are *homeomorphism*: for the examples (b), (d), (e), (f) it suffices to note that the mapping point $\to$ character, being obviously continuous, is automatically bicontinuous; the case of (c) is deduced from case (b) by considering $\tilde{A}$.

§ 2.2. *The Gelfand transformation*

First let A be a C. B. A. with unit; for all $x \in A$ we denote by $\hat{x}_A$ or more simply by $\hat{x}$ the complex function on $\hat{A}$ defined by

$$\hat{x}(\chi) = \chi(x);$$

it is continuous from the definition of the topology of A; the set of its values is exactly the spectrum of x, whence

$$\|\hat{x}\| = \sup |\hat{x}(\chi)| = \nu(x). \tag{i}$$

Now if A has no unit, for all $x \in A$ we also denote by $\hat{x}$ the complex function on $\hat{A}$: $\chi \to \chi(x)$; it is the restriction to $\hat{A}$ of the function $\hat{x}_{\tilde{A}}$ and hence it tends to 0 at infinity; moreover sp x is equal to the union of the set of values of $\hat{x}$ and of the set $\{0\}$; (1) still holds.

The mapping $x \to \hat{x}$ is called the *Gelfand transformation*; it is a morphism of A into the algebra $\mathscr{C}_0(\hat{A})$, continuous and of norm $\leqq 1$; if A has a unit, we have $\hat{e} = 1$. In short

Theorem 2.2. The Gelfand transformation $x \to \hat{x}$ defined by $\hat{x}(\chi) = \chi(x)$ is a continuous morphism with norm $\leqq 1$ of A into $\mathscr{C}_0(\hat{A})$; for all x

$$\|\hat{x}\| = \nu(x) = \lim_{n\to\infty} \|x^n\|^{1/n};$$

the set of values of $\hat{x}$ is equal to the spectrum of x, eventually without the number 0 if A has no unit.

We denote by $\mathscr{F}A$ the image of A under the said transformation.

Remark 2.2. The topology of $\hat{A}$ defined in § 2.1 is still the least fine topology which makes the functions $\hat{x}$ continuous; hence, in order that a mapping T from a topological space Z into $\hat{A}$ be continous, it is necessary and sufficient that all the functions $z \to (T(z))\,(x) = \hat{x}\,(T(z))$, where $x \in A$, be continuous.

Remark 2.3. The Gelfand transformation is in general neither surjective nor injective; its image $\mathcal{F}A$ is in general neither closed nor everywhere dense in $\mathscr{C}_0(\hat{A})$; in order that it be isometric it is necessary and sufficient that we have $\|x^2\| = \|x^2\|$ for all x.

Remark 2.4. Let us suppose A is unitary; if f is a rational fraction regular on sp x, we can define $f(x)$: f is of form P/Q, where Q is not equal to zero on sp x; $Q(x)$ is invertible (cf. Corollary 1.9) and $f(x) = P(x)\,(Q(x))^{-1}$; we then readily obtain $\widehat{f(x)} = f \circ \hat{x}$ whence it follows that $\operatorname{sp} f(x) = f(\operatorname{sp} x)$.

Remark 2.5. Using the notations above let us suppose that A is the full closed subalgebra generated by x and e; let us identify $\hat{A}$ with sp x; then $\widehat{f(x)}$ is the restriction of f to sp x; now if y is an arbitrary element of A, $\hat{y}$ is the uniform limit of restrictions of rational fractions regular on sp x. Similarly, if A is the closed subalgebra generated by x and e, and e, any function $\hat{y}$ is a uniform limit of restrictions of polynomials.

§ 2.3. *The radical*

We recall that we call the *radical* of a C. B. A. A the intersection of its regular maximal ideals; it is hence a *closed ideal*; it is also

- the intersection of the kernels of the characters
- the kernel of the Gelfand transformation
- the set of elements whose spectrum is reduced to $\{0\}$
- the set of elements x such that $\nu(x) = \lim\limits_{n \to \infty} \|x^n\|^{1/n} = 0$.

It is clear that rad A contains all the nilpotent elements – – – which explains why the elements of rad A are sometimes called "quasi-nilpotent" or "generalized nilpotent". Note that rad A is independent of the topology of A: same comment as that following Theorem 2.1.

Examples. The algebras of the examples (a) to (f) obviously have no radical; that of example (g) also has no radical by virtue of Remark 2.3. On the contrary, in example (i) the radical is equal to the algebra.

Proposition 2.2. A morphism from a C. B. A. into a C. B. A. without radical is continuous.

Let $T : A \to B$ be the morphism in question; from the closed-graph theorem (cf. [7]) it suffices to prove that the graph of T in $A \times B$ is closed; let thus (x, y) be an element of $A \times B$ adherent to the graph of T; to show that $y = Tx$ it suffices to show that $\chi\,(y - Tx) = 0$ for all $\chi \in \hat{B}$; now for all $\varepsilon > 0$ there is an $x' \in A$ such that

$$\|x' - x\| \leqq \varepsilon,\ \|Tx' - y\| \leqq \varepsilon;$$

then $|\chi\,(Tx' - y)| \in \varepsilon$; but $\chi \circ T$ is either zero or a character of A and we have $|\chi\,(Tx' - Tx)| \leqq \varepsilon$, whence $|\chi\,(y - Tx)| \leqq 2\varepsilon$ and, since ε is arbitrary, $\chi(y - Tx) = 0$.

Corollary 2.1. There is at most one Banach algebra topology on a commutative algebra without radical.

Exercises

1. The radical of a unitary C. B. A. is the set of x such that $e + xy$ is invertible for all y.

2. There is no norm on the algebra of indefinitely differentiable complex functions over [0, 1] which makes it a Banach algebra.

[Otherwise there would exist, for any integer $m > 0$, a number c_m such that $\sup\limits_{x \in [0,1]} |f^{(m)}(x)| \leqq c_m \|f\|$ for all f; construct a function f satisfying $|f^{(m)}(0)| \geqq mc_m$ for all m.]

§ 2.4. *Duality between A and $\hat{A}$.*

(We assume $\hat{A}$ is non-empty).

The function $(x, \chi) \to \chi(x) = \hat{x}(\chi)$ establishes a certain "duality" between A and $\hat{A}$.

For any subset D of A we denote by $h(D)$ (h for "hull") the closed set of the characters which are zero on D; $h(D)$ is also the intersection of the $\hat{x}^{-1}(0)$ for $x \in D$; or finally, if we speak of regular maximal ideals, the set of regular maximal ideals containing D.

For any subset E of $\hat{A}$ we denote by $k(E)$ (k for "kernel") the closed ideal of A, intersection of the kernels of the $\chi \in E$; it is also the set of x such that $\hat{x}$ is zero on E.

It is clear that the mappings h and k are decreasing and that on the other hand we always have $k(h(D)) \supset D$ and $h(k(E)) \supset E$; hence we always have

$$h(k(h(D))) = h(D) \quad \text{and} \quad k(h(k(E))) = k(E).$$

We are going to prove that the sets E of $\hat{A}$ which satisfy $E = h(k(E))$ are the closed sets for a certain topology; first of all, they are the sets of the form $h(D)$ and we can impose on D that it be a closed ideal; $\varnothing$ and $\hat{A}$ are closed since $\varnothing = h(A)$ and $\hat{A} = h(\{0\})$; then if (E_i) is a family of closed sets with $E_i = h(D_i)$, D_i a closed ideal of A, $\bigcap E_i = h(\bigcup D_i)$ is closed; finally if the family (E_i) is finite, $\bigcup E_i$ is closed; indeed, we obviously have $\bigcup E_i \subset h(\bigcap D_i)$; we also have $\bigcup E_i \supset h(\bigcap D_i)$ because if $\chi \notin \bigcup E_i$ there exists for all i an element x_i of D_i such that $\chi(x_i) \neq 0$; then we have $\chi(\prod x_i) \neq 0$ and $\prod x_i \in \bigcap D_i$; which proves that $\chi \notin h(\bigcap D_i)$.

Definition. We call the *hk-topology* (or "hull-kernel"), the topology in A for which the closed sets are the sets $h(D)$, where D is an arbitrary subset of A which can always be replaced by a closed ideal; in other words a subset of $\hat{A}$ is hk-closed if and only if it is defined by the vanishing of a family of functions $\hat{x}$. The closure of an arbitrary subset E is the set $h(k(E))$ of points where all the functions $\hat{x}$ which vanish on E vanish.

This topology is not as fine as the topology of simple convergence defined in § 2.1; in Chapter V, we will study, under the name of "regular" algebras, the algebras for which these two topologies coincide; it is already clear that the algebras of examples (b), (c), (e) enter into this cathegory; the same is obviously not true of example (d): *a* hk-closed subset of Δ distinct from Δ can meet a disc $|z| \leq u$, $u < 1$, only in a finite number of points; this example shows that the hk-topology is in general *non-separated*; moreover, for a unitary C. B. A., it can be separated only if it coincides with the topology of simple convergence.

We note in passing that for a ring A one defines ([5]) a topology (said to be "spectral" or "Zariski") analogous to this one, but on the set of prime ideals of A.

Let us now examine the other aspect of the duality between A and $\hat{A}$; if D is a subset of A, $k(h(D))$ is the intersection of the regular maximal ideals containing D; we can have $D = k(h(D))$ only if D is a closed ideal; but this condition is far from being sufficient; finding conditions for a closed ideal I to satisfy $I = k(h(I))$, or, in other words, to be the intersection of regular maximal ideals, is one of the most important and most difficult problems in the theory of commutative Banach algebras; it is closely related to that of Spectral Synthesis in Harmonic Analysis and will be approached here on several occasions (§§ 5.3 and 7.4). A trivial example of a closed ideal which is not the intersection of regular maximal ideals is provided by the ideal $\{0\}$ of a C. B. A. with a non-zero radical.

Examples

(b) and (c): all closed ideals are intersections of regular maximal ideals (cf. § 1.5).

(d): in [16], Chapter **6**, one will find examples of closed ideals which are not intersections of regular maximal ideals.

(e): let x be a point of $[0, 1]$; the closed ideal composed of the f satisfying $f(x) = f'(x) = 0$ is contained in only one maximal ideal --- that which corresponds to x --- and is not equal to it; see also § 5.4.

(f): there exist closed ideals which are not intersections of maximal ideals (cf. [32]).

Exercises

1. Any subset of $\hat{A}$ reduced to a point is hk-closed,

2. If A is unitary, $\hat{A}$ is hk-quasi-compact (i.e. verifies the Borel-Lebesgue axiom).

3. Example of a spectrum $\hat{A}$ which is quasi-compact but not locally quasi-compact for the hk-topology. Let D be the open subset of $\mathfrak{C}$ defined by the conditions $x^2 + y^2 < 1$ and $|y| < (1 - x)^2$ and let A be the algebra of the functions continuous on $\bar{D}$ and holomorphic on D; A is generated by the function $z \to z$ [show as in § 1.5, example (d), that any function of A is the uniform limit of functions holomorphic in the neighbourhood of $\bar{D}$; then assume that such a function is a uniform limit on $\bar{D}$ of polynomials, which will be proved in § 6.3,

no. 4]; we can hence identify $\hat{A}$ with D and an arbitrary element f of A with $\hat{f}$. Show that the neighbourhood $\overline{D} - \{1\}$ of 0 does not contain any quasi-compact neighbourhood [let E be a subset of $\overline{D} - \{1\}$ containing an open neighbourhood V of 0; for any $a > 0$ let E_a be the set of numbers $1 - a/n\pi$ (n an integer $\geqq a/2\pi$); there exists an a_0 such that $E_{a_0} \subset V$; then for any integer $p > 0$ we have $E_{a_0/2^p} \subset E$; $E_{a_0/2^p} \cup \{1\}$ is the set of zeros of the function $z \to (1 - z) \sin (a_0/2^p (1 - z))$, hence $E_{a_0/2^p}$ is closed in E; the $E_{a_0/2^p}$ are decreasing and their intersection is empty].

§ 2.5. *Šilov boundary*

(In this section and those following, all topological concepts are, unless specifically mentioned otherwise, relative to the topology of simple convergence).

The concept of boundary described here admits numerous variations which will be dealt with in a later Seminar; in § 6.2, no. 2, we will see that it is connected to that of the extreme point of a subset of a vector space.

Theorem 2.3 (Šilov). Let A be a commutative Banach algebra; there exists in $\hat{A}$ a smallest closed subset on which all the functions $|\hat{x}|$ $(x \in A)$ reach their maximum.

Let $\mathcal{F}$ be the set (non-empty since it contains $\hat{A}$) of the closed subsets of $\hat{A}$ on which all the functions $|x|$ reach their maximum; if we order it by setting $F_1 \leqq F_2$ when $F_1 \supset F_2$, $\mathcal{F}$ is inductive: indeed, let $\mathcal{F}_0$ be a totally ordered subset of $\mathcal{F}$ and let $F_0 = \bigcap F$ for $F \in \mathcal{F}_0$; for all x which does not belong to the radical of A the set F_x of the points where $|\hat{x}|$ reaches its maximum is compact and meets each $F \in \mathcal{F}_0$; hence F_x meets F_0 and $F_0 \in \mathcal{F}$.

By Zorn's theorem, $\mathcal{F}$ admits at least one minimal element F_1 for the relation $\subset$; we will see that F_1 is the smallest element of $\mathcal{F}$.

To do this we must prove that if $F_2 \in \mathcal{F}$ then $F_1 \subset F_2$, that is to say that any point χ_1 of F_1 is adherent to F_2; a neighbourhood of χ_1 contains a neighbourhood V defined by conditions

$$|\hat{x}_i(\chi) - \hat{x}_i(\chi_1)| < 1 \qquad i = 1, \ldots, n;$$

if we set $y_i = x_i - \hat{x}_i(\chi_1)e$ (e = unit element of $\tilde{A}$), V is also defined by the conditions

$$|\hat{y}_i(\chi)| < 1 \qquad i = 1, \ldots, n;$$

since F_1 is minimal in $\mathcal{F}$ there existe a $y \in A$ such that

$$1 = \sup_{\chi \in V} |\hat{y}(\chi)| > \sup_{\chi \in F_1 - F_1 \cap V} |\hat{y}(\chi)|$$

and, eventually replacing y by one of its powers, we can assume

$$\sup_{\chi \in F_1 - F_1 \cap V} |\hat{y}(\chi)| < 1/\sup \|y_i\|.$$

The function $|\hat{y}|$ reaches its maximum 1 at at least one point χ_2 of F_2; on the other hand we have, for all i : $yy_i \in A$ and $|\hat{y}(\chi)| \cdot |\hat{y}_i(\chi)| < 1$ for all $\chi \in V$ and all $\chi \in F_1 - F_1 \cap V$, hence for all $\varkappa$ and in particular for $\chi = \chi_2$; but this implies that $|\hat{y}_i(\chi_2)| < 1$ for all i, that is that $\chi_2 \in V$; finally $F_2 \cap V \neq \varnothing$. Q. E. D.

The subset of $\hat{A}$ defined by the previous theorem is called the *boundary of* A (or *Šilov boundary* since there exist other concepts of boundary) and will be denoted by bdry A.

Remark 2.6. The proof of the previous theorem also proves the following result: if X is a compact space and B is a subalgebra of $\mathcal{C}(X)$ which separates the points of X, there is a smallest closed subset of X on which all the functions of B reach their maximum modulus; this result does not hold if we do not assume B is separating: consider for instance the algebra of the even continuous functions on $[-1, 1]$.

Lemma 2.1. A point χ_0 of $\hat{A}$ belongs to bdry A if and only if for any neighbourhood V of χ_0 there is an $x \in A$ satisfying.

$$\sup_{\varkappa \in V} |\hat{x}(\chi)| > \sup_{\varkappa \in \hat{A} - V} |\hat{x}(\chi)|.$$

The condition is necessary because V contains an open neighbourhood U of χ_0 and $\hat{A} - U$ is a closed set which does not contain bdry A. It is sufficient because if it holds any neighbourhood of χ_0 meets bdry A.

Proposition 2.3. Let us suppose that A is the full closed subalgebra generated by x and e and let us identify $\hat{A}$ with sp x as shown in Proposition 2.1; then bdry A is identified with the topological boundary of sp x in $\mathfrak{C}$.

We know (Remark 2.5) that the functions $\hat{x}$ are holomorphic on the interior of sp x; we have thus bdry $A \subset$ top. bdry. of sp x by virtue of the theorem of the maximum modulus. Conversely, let us take a point z_0 of the topological boundary and show that for any neighbourhood V of z_0 in sp x there exists a $y \in A$ such that

$$\sup_{z \in V} |\hat{y}(z)| > \sup_{z \in \operatorname{sp} x - V} |\hat{y}(z)|;$$

V contains the intersection of sp x with a disc $|z - z_0| < r$; then there exists *a* $z_1 \in \mathfrak{C} - \operatorname{sp} x$ such that $|z_0 - z_1| < r/3$; the element $(x - z_1 e)^{-1}$ has as its Gelfand transform the function $z \to 1/(z - z_1)$, whose modulus takes the value $3/r$ at z_0 and values $\leqq 3/2r$ on sp $x - V$.

Examples

It is obvious that for the examples (b), (c) and (e), the boundary is identical to the spectrum; for example (d) it coincides with the circle $|z| = 1$ and for the example (f) with the spectrum, by virtue of the previous proposition.

Exercise

We assume A is unitary and the Gelfand transformation is isometric; then the topological divisors of zero are the x such that $\hat{x}$ vanishes at least once on bdry A; and bdry A is the smallest subset of A on which the Gelfand transform of all topological divisors of zero vanishes at least once.

§ 2.6. *Spectra of subalgebras, ideals, quotients, etc.*

Proposition 2.4. Let A be *a* C. B. A. with unit e, B *a* closed subalgebra containing e, T the mapping $\chi \to \chi/B$ of $\hat{A}$ into $\hat{B}$, R the equivalence relation on $\hat{A}$ defined by T; then T goes to the quotient in a homeomorphism of $\hat{A}/R$ onto $T(\hat{A})$; moreover $T(\hat{A})$ is closed in $\hat{B}$ and contains the boundary of B.

$$\begin{array}{ccl} \hat{A} & \xrightarrow{T} & T(\hat{A}) \subset \hat{B} \\ \downarrow & \nearrow & \\ \hat{A}/R & & \end{array}$$

The first assertion follows from the continuity of T; in order to prove the second it suffices, since $T(\hat{A})$ is compact, to prove that each function $|\hat{x}|$ on $\hat{B}$ ($x \in B$) reaches its maximum on $T(\hat{A})$; now

$$\sup_{\sigma \in T(\hat{A})} |\hat{x}(\sigma)| = \sup_{\chi \in \hat{A}} |\hat{x}(\chi)| = \lim \|x^n\|^{1/n} = \sup_{\sigma \in \hat{B}} |\hat{x}(\sigma)|$$

Corollary 2.2. If bdry $B = \hat{B}$, $\hat{B}$ is homeomorphic to $\hat{A}/R$.

Example. Consider the algebra of example (d) as a subalgebra of the algebra of continuous functions on the circle $|z| = 1$.

Proposition 2.5. Let I be a closed ideal of a C. B. A. A; the mapping $\chi \to \chi/I$ establishes a homeomorphism between $\hat{A} - h(I)$ and $\hat{I}$; for all $x \in I$ this homeomorphism makes the function $\hat{x}$ on $\hat{I}$ correspond to the function $\hat{x} \mid \hat{A} - h(I)$.

For any $\chi \in A - h(I)$ let us set $T(\chi) = \chi \mid I$; T is
- obviously continuous
- injective, because if $T(\chi) = T(\chi')$ there is an $x \in I$ such that $\chi(x) = \chi'(x) \neq 0$; then for all $y \in A$ we have

$$\chi(x) = \chi(xy) \;/\; \chi(x) = \chi'(xy) \;/\; \chi'(x) = \chi'(y)$$

- surjective, since any character χ of I extends into a character $\tilde{\chi}$ of A defined by taking $x \in I$, $\chi(x) \neq 0$, and by setting $\chi(y) = \chi(xy)/\chi(x)$
- bicontinuous: it suffices (Remark 2.2) to show that all the mappings $\chi \to \chi(y)$, where $y \in A$, are continuous - - - which is more or less obvious.

Proposition 2.6. Using the notations of Proposition 2.5, the passage to the quotient establishes a homeomorphism between $h(I)$ and $\widehat{A/I}$; for all $x \in A$ this homeomorphism makes the function $\hat{\hat{x}}$ on $\widehat{A/I}$ correspond to the function $\hat{x} \mid h(I)$.

The proof is immediate.

Example. In the case of example (c), any closed ideal I is canonically identified with $\mathscr{C}_0(X - h(I))$ and A/I with $\mathscr{C}_0(h(I))$.

Remark 2.7. We can see that the spectra of the closed ideals (resp. the quotients) of A are exactly the open sets (resp. the closed sets) of $\hat{A}$ for the hk-topology.

Remark 2.8. The propositions 2.5 and 2.6 allow us to say that if A is an extension of $B = A/I$ by I, $\hat{A}$ is an extension of $\hat{B}$ by $\hat{I}$ in the following sense: $\hat{A}$ admits a partition composed of an open subset homeomorphic to $\hat{I}$ and a closed subset homeomorphic to $\hat{B}$; the problem of classifying the extensions of the C. B. A. is hence connected with that of the classification of the extensions of the topological spaces in the sense indicated.

Proposition 2.7. If A is a direct sum of two closed ideals I_1 and I_2, $\hat{A}$ is homeomorphic to the topological sum of $\hat{I}_1$ and $\hat{I}_2$.

Indeed $h(I_1)$ and $h(I_2)$ are disjoint and on the other hand they cover $\hat{A}$ since otherwise there would be a character of A which vanishes neither on I_1 nor on I_2, and is hence non-vanishing on $I_1 \cap I_2$, which is absurd. Q. E. D.

This result will be made more precise by Corollary 4.2.

Tensor products

Let A_1 and A_2 be two C. B. A.; we first recall the definition of the C. B. A. $A_1 \otimes A_2$; on the algebra $A_1 \underset{\text{alg}}{\otimes} A_2$, algebraic tensor product of A_1 by A_2, we define a norm by setting

$$\|x\| = \inf \sum \|x_{1,i}\| \cdot \|x_{2,i}\|$$

where the lower bound is taken for all the sequences $(x_{1,i}, x_{2,i})_{i=1,\ldots,n}$ satisfying

$$x = \sum x_{1,i} \otimes x_{2,i};$$

The norm axioms are readily verified and $A_1 \otimes A_2$ is by definition the completed algebra of $A_1 \underset{\text{alg}}{\otimes} A_2$ for this norm.

Now if χ_1 and χ_2 are characters of A_1 and A_2, the bilinear form $(x_1, x_2) \to \chi_1(x_1) \cdot \chi_2(x_2)$ defines canonically a linear form $\chi_1 \underset{\text{alg}}{\otimes} \chi_2$ on $A_1 \underset{\text{alg}}{\otimes} A_2$, satisfying

$$(\chi_1 \underset{\text{alg}}{\otimes} \chi_2) \left(\sum x_{1,i} \otimes x_{2,i}\right) = \sum \chi_1(x_{1,i}) \cdot \chi_2(x_{2,i});$$

we readily see that this linear form is a morphism of algebras and that it is continuous; it extends thus into a character of $A_1 \otimes A_2$ which we denote by $\chi_1 \otimes \chi_2$. We then have the

Proposition 2.8. The mapping $(\chi_1, \chi_2) \to \chi_1 \otimes \chi_2$ is a homeomorphism of $\hat{A}_1 \times \hat{A}_2$ onto $\widehat{A_1 \otimes A_2}$.

The mapping T is:

- injective: suppose $\chi_1 \otimes \chi_2 = \chi_1' \otimes \chi_2'$; let $x_2 \notin \operatorname{Ker} \chi_2$; the equality

$$\chi_1(x_1) \cdot \chi_2(x_2) = \chi_1'(x_1) \cdot \chi_2'(x_2),$$

valid for all $x_1 \in A_1$, shows that $\operatorname{Ker} \chi_1' \subset \operatorname{Ker} \chi_1$, hence $\chi_1' = \chi_1$ and similarly $\chi_2' = \chi_2$;

- surjective: let χ be a character of $A_1 \otimes A_2$; it does not vanish on all the elements $y_1 \otimes y_2$ since they generate $A_1 \otimes A_2$; let thus y_1 and y_2 be such that $\chi\,(y_1 \otimes y_2) \neq 0$; for all $x_1 \in A_1$ and all $x_2 \in A_2$ let us set

$$\chi_1(x_1) = \chi(x_1 y_1 \otimes y_2) \,/\, \chi(y_1 \otimes y_2)$$

$$\chi_2(x_2) = \chi(y_1 \otimes x_2 y_2) \,/\, \chi(y_1 \otimes y_2);$$

it follows readily that χ_1 and χ_2 are characters and $\chi = \chi_1 \otimes \chi_2$;

- continuous: it is clear that it is if we endow $\widehat{A_1 \otimes A_2}$ with the topology of simple convergence on $A_1 \underset{\text{alg}}{\otimes} A_2$; but this topology is identical to the topology of simple convergence on $A_1 \otimes A_2$ since $\widehat{A_1 \otimes A_2}$ is an equicontinuous subset of $\mathscr{E}\,(A_1 \otimes A_2)$;

- bicontinuous: it suffices to note that the mappings $\chi \to \chi_1$ and $\chi \to \chi_2$ defined above are continuous, and we can resume the reasoning in Proposition 2.5.

Exercises

1. Generalize Proposition 2.4 to the case where A and B are no longer assumed unitary.

2. Let A be a C. B. A. with unit e, I a closed ideal of A, A' a closed subalgebra containing e and supplémentary to I; show that $h(I)$ is a retract of $\hat{A}$.

Problem: does this result admit a converse?

§ 2.7. *Simultaneous spectra*

Definition. Let A be a commutative Banach algebra with unit and $a_1, \ldots, a_n$ elements of A; we call the *simultaneous spectrum* of $a_1, \ldots, a_n$ and we denote by $\mathrm{sp}_A(a_1, \ldots, a_n)$ or $\mathrm{sp}(a_1, \ldots, a_n)$ the set of points $(\lambda_1, \ldots, \lambda_n)$ of $\mathfrak{C}^n$ such that $a_1 - \lambda_1 e, \ldots, e_n - \lambda_n e$ belong to the same maximal ideal; or again the set of points $(\chi(a_1), \ldots, \chi(a_n))$ for $\chi \in \hat{A}$.

The complementary set of $\mathrm{sp}(a_1, \ldots, a_n)$ is the set of $(\lambda_1, \ldots, \lambda_n)$ such that the ideal generated by $a_1 - \lambda_1 e, \ldots, a_n - \lambda_n e$ is A; that is also, such that there exist $b_1, \ldots, b_n \in A$ satisfying

$$\sum_{i=1}^{n} (a_i - \lambda_i e) b_i = e$$

The set $\mathrm{sp}(a_1, \ldots, a_n)$ is non-empty since A admits at least one character, and is compact since it is the image of $\hat{A}$ under the mapping $\chi \to (\chi(a_1), \ldots, \chi(a_n))$; it is in fact contained in the product of the $\mathrm{sp}\, a_i$. For any polynomial P we have

$$sp\,(P(a_1, \ldots, a_n)) = P(sp(a_1, \ldots, a_n));$$

hence if f is a rational fraction regular on $\mathrm{sp}(a_1, \ldots, a_n)$, $f(a_1, \ldots, a_n)$ exists and we have $\mathrm{sp}(f(a_1, \ldots, a_n)) = f(\mathrm{sp}(a_1, \ldots, a_n))$. Note that if $p \leqq n$ and if we write $\mathfrak{C}^n = \mathfrak{C}^p \times \mathfrak{C}^{n-p}$, $\mathrm{sp}(a_1, \ldots, a_n)$ is the projection of $\mathrm{sp}(a_1, \ldots, a_n)$ on $\mathfrak{C}^p$; finally we note that if we have a morphism T of A into another C. B. A. A' transforming a unit into a unit, we have $\mathrm{sp}_{A'}(Ta_1, \ldots, Ta_n) \subset \mathrm{sp}_A(a_1, \ldots, a_n)$; in particular the greater the ambient algebra, the smaller the simultaneous spectrum.

Proposition 2.9. If A is the full closed subalgebra generated by $a_1, \ldots, a_n$ and e, the mapping $\chi \to (\chi(a_1), \ldots, \chi(a_n))$ of $\hat{A}$ onto $\mathrm{sp}(a_1, \ldots, a_n)$ is a homeomorphism.

The proof is immediate.

Definitions. For any compact subset X of $\mathfrak{C}^n$ we will denote by $\mathcal{P}(X)$ (resp. $\mathcal{R}(X)$ the closure in $\mathcal{C}(X)$ of the set of restrictions to X of polynomials (resp. of rational fractions regular on X).

Remark 2.9. With the hypotheses of Proposition 2.9, let us identify $\hat{A}$ to $\mathrm{sp}(a_1, \ldots, a_n)$; the function $\hat{a}_i$ on $\hat{A}$ becomes the ith coordinate function; for any rational fraction f which is regular on A, $\widehat{f(a_1, \ldots, a_n)}$ becomes the restriction of f to $\hat{A}$; finally if $x \in A$, $\hat{x}$ is the uniform limit on $\hat{A}$ of restrictions of rational fractions regular on $\hat{A}$; in other words $\mathcal{F}A \subset \mathcal{R}(\hat{A})$.

Similarly we see that if A is the closed subalgebra generated by $a_1, \ldots, a_n$ and e, we get $\mathcal{F}A \subset \mathcal{P}(\hat{A})$.

Remark 2.10. Proposition 2.3 does not generalize to the case of several generators (cf. § 6.3, no. 3).

Proposition 2.10. If A is the closed (resp. full closed) subalgebra generated by $a_1, \ldots, a_n$ and e, $\operatorname{sp}(a_1, \ldots, a_n)$ is polynomially (resp. rationally) convex.

We prove for instance the first assertion: let $z^0 = (z_1^0, \ldots, z_n^0) \in \mathcal{C}^n - \operatorname{sp}(a_1, \ldots, a_n)$ and let $b_1, \ldots, b_n \in A$ be such that $\sum (z_1^0 e - a_i) b_i = e$; there exist polynomials $P_1, \ldots, P_n$ such that

$$\left\|\sum (z_i^0 e - a_i) \cdot P_i(a_1, \ldots, a_n) - e\right\| < 1;$$

if we identify $\hat{A}$ with $\operatorname{sp}(a_1, \ldots, a_n)$, the element of the first member has the following polynomial as its Gelfand transform

$$z \to \sum (z_i^0 - z_i) \cdot P_i(z_1, \ldots, z_n) - 1$$

which hence assumes on $\operatorname{sp}(a_1, \ldots, a_n)$ values with modulus strictly less than 1; on the other hand it takes the value -1 at z^0.

Corollary 2.3. A compact subset X of $\mathfrak{C}$ is polynomially convex if and only if its complement is connected.

The condition is necessary by virtue of the maximum modulus principle; conversely, let us assume it holds; let g be the element $z \to z$ of $\mathcal{P}(X)$; since g generates $\mathcal{P}(X)$ is suffices to show that $\operatorname{sp} g = X$; we obviously have $\operatorname{sp} g \supset X$; then $\operatorname{sp} g - X$ is closed in $\mathfrak{C} - X$; $(\mathfrak{C} - X) - (\operatorname{sp} g - X) = \mathfrak{C} - \operatorname{sp} g$ is non-empty and closed in $\mathfrak{C} - X$; indeed suppose $\lambda_n \in \mathfrak{C} - \operatorname{sp} g$ and $\lambda_n \to \lambda \in \operatorname{sp} g - X$; $g - \lambda e$ is a topological divisor of zero (proposition 1.3), i.e. there is an $f_n \in \mathcal{P}(X)$ with $\|f_n\| \geqq 1$ and $f_n(z) \cdot (z - \lambda) \to 0$ uniformly on X --- which is absurd; finally $\mathfrak{C} - \operatorname{sp} g$ is non-empty, open and closed in $\mathfrak{C} - X$, hence equal to $\mathfrak{C} - X$.

Proposition 2.11. Conversely, any polynomially (resp. rationally) convex compact subset X of $\mathfrak{C}^n$ is the simultaneous spectrum of n

generators in the "closed subalgebra" sense (resp. "full closed subalgebra" sense) of a unitary C. B. A., namely $\mathscr{P}(X)$ (resp. $\mathscr{R}(X)$).

Let us prove for instance the first assertion; the algebra $\mathscr{P}(X)$ is generated by the coordinate functions a_i and by 1; we obviously have $X \subset \text{sp}(a_1, \ldots, a_n)$; to show that equality holds, let us take a point $z^0 \notin X$, then a polynomial P such that

$$|P(z^\circ)| > \sup_{z \in X} |P(z)|; \tag{1}$$

if z^0 belonged to $\text{sp}(a_1, \ldots, a_n)$, there would be a character χ of $\mathscr{P}(X)$ such that $\chi(a_i) = z_i^0$; then $\chi(P \mid X) = P(z^0)$ – – – which contradicts (1). Q. E. D.

In Chapter IV we will use the following lemma:

Lemma 2.2. Given an open neighbourhood U of $\text{sp}_A(a_1, \ldots, a_n)$, we can find elements $a_{n+1}, \ldots, a_{n+p}$ such that, denoting by A' the closed subalgebra generated by $e, a_1, \ldots, a_{n+p}$, we have

$$\text{sp}_A(a_1, \ldots, a_n) \subset \text{sp}_{A'}(a_1, \ldots, a_n) \subset U.$$

For any A', $\text{sp}_{A'}(a_1, \ldots, a_n)$ will be contained in the polydisc $|z_1| \leqq \|a_1\|, \ldots, |z_n| \leqq \|a_n\|$, which we denote by K. If $z \in K - K \cap U$, there exist $w_1(z), \ldots, w_n(z) \in A$ such that

$$\sum (z_i e - a_i)\, w_i(z) = e;$$

for z' sufficiently close to z, say for $z' \in V_z$, an open neighbourhood of z, $\sum (z_i' e - a_i) w_i(z)$ has an inverse equal to

$$\sum_{k=0}^{\infty} (e - \sum_{i=1}^{n} (z_i' - a_i)\, w_i(z))^k$$

and which hence belongs to the closed subalgebra generated by e, $a_1, \ldots, a_n, w_1(z), \ldots, w_n(z)$. Let $z^1, \ldots, z^q$ be such that $V_{z^1}, \ldots, V_{z^q}$ cover $K - K \cap U$; let us take as the elements $a_{n+1}, \ldots, a_{n+p}$ the elements $w_i(z^j)$ for $i = 1, \ldots, n$ and $j = 1, \ldots, q$; if $z' \in K - K \cap U$, z' belongs to a V_{z^j}, hence $\sum_i (z_i' e - a_i) w_i(z^j)$ is invertible in A' and $z \notin \text{sp}_{A'}(a_1, \ldots, a_n)$. Q. E. D.

The interest of this lemma lies in the fact that $\text{sp}(a_1, \ldots, a_n)$ "differs as little as we please" from $\text{sp}_{A'}(a_1, \ldots, a_n)$, which is the projection of the *polynomially convex* set $\text{sp}_{A'}(a_1, \ldots, a_{n+p})$.

Exercises

1. We suppose that A is the closed (resp. full closed) subalgebra generated by $a_1, \ldots, a_n$ and e; we suppose further that the Gelfand transformation is isometric; then A is isomorphic to $\mathscr{P}(\hat{A})$ (resp. $\mathscr{R}(\hat{A})$).

2. Example of three C. B. A. A, A_1, A_2 such that $A \subset A_1 \subset A_2$ and $\hat{A} = \hat{A}_2 \neq \hat{A}_1$. Denote by A the algebra of example (d), $A_2 = \mathscr{C}(\Delta)$, A_1 the closed subalgebra of A_2 generated by A and by the function $z \to |z|$; show that $\hat{A}_1$ is homeomorphic to the subset E of $\mathfrak{R}^3$ defined by the conditions

$$x_1^2 + x_2^2 \leqq x_3^2; \; 0 \leqq x_3 \leqq 1.$$

[Consider the subalgebra A_1' of A_2 algebraically generated by the functions $z \to z$, $z \to |z|$, $z \to 1$; construct an isomorphism of A_1 onto a subalgebra B of $\mathscr{C}(E)$; show that $\hat{B} = \mathrm{sp}_B(a_1, a_2) = E$ where a_1 and a_2 respectively denote the functions $(x_1, x_2, x_3) \to x_1 + ix_2$ and $(x_1, x_2, x_3) \to x_3$.]

CHAPTER III

HOLOMORPHIC FUNCTIONAL CALCULUS WITH ONE VARIABLE

We denote by A a commutative Banach algebra with unit element e. For all $a \in A$ and all rational fractions f regular on sp a, $f(a)$ has the meaning described in Remark 2.4; the equality $\widehat{f(a)} = f \circ \hat{a}$ shows that if A is without radical, $f(a)$ only depends on the values assumed by f on sp a (this is not true if A has a non-zero radical; take a in the radical and the rational fractions $z \to 0$ and $z \to z$). In the chapter we will extend the functional calculus to more general functions: the functions holomorphic in the neighbourhood of sp a; in fact in certain cases it can be extended to even more general functions: see for instance §§ 7.4 and 8.2. For this purpose we will use the theory of holomorphic functions with values in Banach spaces, in particular the Cauchy integral formula and the residue theorem.

The element $f(a)$ will temporarily be denoted $T_a(\tilde{f})$ and it will be understood that with this notation $\tilde{f}$ will always denote the *germ of f in the neighbourhood of sp a* (see Appendix II).

Theorem 3.1. Let a be an element of A; there is a unique continuous morphism T_a of $\mathcal{O}$(sp a) into A transforming the germ of the function 1 into e and that of the function $z \to z$ into a; it has moreover the following properties:

(i) if f is a rational fraction regular on sp a, we have $T_a(\tilde{f}) = f(a)$;

(ii) if A is the field of complex numbers, we have $T_a(\tilde{f}) = f(a)$;

(iii) if L is a continuous morphism of A into a C. B. A. B transforming the unit element of A into that of B, we have $L(T_a(\tilde{f})) = T_{\mathrm{La}}(\tilde{f})$ for any function f holomorphic in the neighbourhood of sp a;

(iv) $\widehat{T_a(\tilde{f})} = f \circ \hat{a}$;

(v) $\mathrm{sp}(T_a(\tilde{f})) = f(\mathrm{sp}\ a)$;

(vi) if g is a function holomorphic in the neighbourhood of the spectrum of $b = T_a(\tilde{f})$ we have $T_b(\tilde{g}) = T_a(\widetilde{g \circ f})$.

Let f be a holomorphic function on an open neighbourhood U of $\mathrm{sp}\ a$; let C be a contour contained in $U - \mathrm{sp}\ a$ and such that $h(z_0) = {}^1/_{(2\pi i)} \cdot \int_C h(z)/(z - z_0) \cdot dz$ for any $z_0 \in \mathrm{sp}\ a$ and any function h holomorphic on U (such a contour is not uniquely defined, but its homology class in $H_1(U - \mathrm{sp}\ a)$ is).

The element ${}^1/_{(2\pi i)} \cdot \int_C f(z) \cdot (ze - a)^{-1}\, dz$ of A does not depend on the choice of C and can hence be denoted by $T_{a,U}(f)$; it is clear that $T_{a,U}$ is a continuous linear mapping of $\mathcal{O}(U)$ into A; then $T_{a,U}(f)$ only depends on the germ $\tilde{f}$ of f in the neighbourhood of $\mathrm{sp}\ a$; indeed, if f' is another function holomorphic on an other open neighbourhood U', equal to f on a third neighbourhood $U'' \subset U \cap U'$, we can choose C in U'' and we get

$$T_{a,U'}(f') = {}^1/_{(2\pi i)} \cdot \int_C f'(z) \cdot (ze - a)^{-1}\, dz$$

$$= {}^1/_{(2\pi i)} \cdot \int_C f(z) \cdot (ze - a)^{-1}\, dz = T_{a,U}(f);$$

The various mappings $T_{a,U}$ define hence a continuous linear mapping T_a of $\mathcal{O}(\mathrm{sp}\ a)$ into A;

$$T_a(\tilde{f}) = {}^1/_{(2\pi i)} \cdot \int_C f(z) \cdot (ze - a)^{-1}\, dz.$$

We will now establish the property (i); let us first suppose that $f(z) = z^n$ (n an integer $\geqq 0$); let us take as our C a circle with centre 0 and radius $> \|a\|$; we have

$$T_a(\tilde{f}) = {}^1/_{(2\pi i)} \cdot \int_C z^{n-1} \cdot \sum_{p=0}^{\infty} a^p/z^p\, dz = a^n;$$

this proves in passing that T_a transforms the germ of the function 1 into e and that of the function z into a; and also that $T_a(\tilde{f}) = f(a)$ is f is a polynomial.

Let us now suppose that $f(z) = (z - u)^{-n}$ ($u \in \mathfrak{C} - \text{sp}\, a$, n an integer > 0) and show that $T_a(f) = (a - ue)^{-n}$; by a simple change of variables we can assume $u = 0$; we take as our C the union of circles of centre 0: C_1 of radius $> \|a\|$ and C_2 of radius smaller than $\|a^{-1}\|^{-1}$ and than the distance from 0 to sp a; we have

$$\int_{C_1} z^{-n}(ze - a)^{-1}\, dz = \int_{C_1} z^{-n-1} \cdot \sum_{p=0}^{\infty} a^p/z^p \cdot dz = 0$$

$$T_a(\tilde{f}) = 1/_{(2\pi i)} \cdot \int_{C_2^-} z^{-n}\, (ze - a)^{-1}\, dz = a^{-1}/2\pi i \cdot \int_{C_2^+} z^{-n}\, (e - a^{-1}z)^{-1}\, dz$$

$$= a^{-1}/2\pi i \cdot \int_{C_2^+} z^{-n} \cdot \sum_{p=0}^{\infty} a^{-p}\, z^p \cdot dz = a^{-n}.$$

Finally using the decomposition into simple elements we obtain the property (i).

Property (ii) can trivially be verified.

To prove the sequel we recall that the germs of rational fractions regular on sp a are everywhere dense in $\mathcal{O}(\text{sp}\, a)$ (it suffices to show that for any relatively campact open set U the rational fractions which are regular on U are everywhere dense in $\mathcal{O}(U)$ and this can be seen by using the Cauchy integral formula); since T_a is continuous and is obviously multiplicative for the germs of rational fractions, T_a is a *morphism*.

Property (iii): the announced equality holds if f is a rational fraction, hence, by continuity, for every f; (iv) follows immediately from (ii) and (iii) applied to the case where $B = \mathfrak{C}$; (v) is a simple consequence of (iv); for (vi) it suffices, by continuity, to prove the assertion in the case where g is a rational fraction, then, by linearity, in each of the following cases:

- $g(z) = z^n$, where n is an integer $\geqq 0$; then

$$T_b(\tilde{g}) = b^n = (T_a(\tilde{f}))^n = T_a(\tilde{f^n}) = T_a(\widetilde{g \circ f})$$

- $g(z) = (z - u)^{-n}$, where n is an integer > 0; then

$$T_b(g) = (b - ue)^{-n} = (T_a(\widetilde{f - u}))^{-n} = T_a((\widetilde{f - u})^{-n}) = T_a(\widetilde{g \circ f}).$$

The uniqueness must still be proved; if S is a continuous morphism of $\mathcal{O}(\text{sp } a)$ into A with the required properties, we have

$$S(\tilde{f}) = f(a) = T_a(\tilde{f})$$

for any rational fraction f, then, by continuity, for any f holomorphic in the neighbourhood of sp a. Q. E. D.

In what follows we will often use the notation $f(a)$ instead of $T_a(\tilde{f})$.

Remark 3.1. If A is *without radical*, property (iv) completely characterizes the mappings T_a and trivially implies the other properties.

Examples. For any element a such that the arg function is univalent on sp a, Theorem 3.1 allows us to construct elements $\log a$; whence elements which are square roots of a, etc.; this is often used in the particular case where sp $a \subset]0, +\infty[$.

Remark 3.2. Suppose f is the sum of a power series $\sum c_n z^n$ with radius of convergence $> \nu(a)$; then $f(a)$ is the limit of the elements $\sum_0^m c_n a^n$, in other words it is the sum of the convergent series $\sum c_n a^n$; this series is even commutatively convergent since the series $\sum c_n z^n$ is; for instance, for $|\lambda| > \nu(a)$ we have $(\lambda e - a)^{-1} = \sum_0^\infty a^n/\lambda^{n+1}$.

If the series $\sum c_n z^n$ has a radius of convergence $> \|a\|$, $f(a)$ is the sum of the *absolutely* convergent series $\sum c_n a^n$ (note that this has already been used in the proof of Theorem 1.1); if the radius of convergence is equal to $\|a\|$ and if the series $\sum c_n z^n$ is still absolutely convergent for $|z| = \|a\|$ we can still define $f(a)$ as equal to $\sum c_n a^n$ (this will be used in the proof of Proposition 7.1).

Example. For all $a \in A$ we can set

$$\exp a = \sum_0^\infty a^n/n!;$$

the mapping exp is continuous and satisfies

$$\exp(a + b) = \exp a \cdot \exp b;$$

its periodicity is studied in [15], Theorem 5.5.5.

Complements

1. The formula $T_{a,U}(f) = {}^1/_{(2\pi i)} \cdot \int_C f(z) \cdot (ze - a)^{-1}\, dz$ is still meaningful if f is a function holomorphic on U with values in A; $T_{a,U}$ is then a morphism $\mathcal{O}(U, A) \to A$ where $\mathcal{O}(U, A)$ denotes the algebra of the functions holomorphic on U with values in A; it is then clear that the various morphisms $T_{a,U}$ define a morphism of $\mathcal{O}(\mathrm{sp}\, a, A)$ into A (where $\mathcal{O}(\mathrm{sp}\, a, A)$ is the inductive limit of the $\mathcal{O}(U, A)$).

2. Other complements will be given at the end of Chapter IV: Taylor formula and properties of the mapping $a \to f(a)$.

Exercise. Let G_1 be the connected component of e in the group of invertible elements of A; show that the exp mapping maps A and G_1 onto G_1.

[First show that exp A is contained in G_1, then that it is open and closed; to show that exp $G_1 = G_1$ use the periodicity of exp.]

It must be mentioned that log x can be defined for all $x \in G_1$ ([15], 5.4).

CHAPTER IV

HOLOMORPHIC FUNCTIONAL CALCULUS WITH SEVERAL VARIABLES

We denote by A a commutative Banach algebra with a unit element e.

§ 4.1. *Preliminaries*

We know what $R(a_1, \ldots, a_n)$ means if $a_1, \ldots, a_n \in A$ and if R is a rational fraction regular on $\mathrm{sp}(a_1, \ldots, a_n)$ (cf. § 2.7); we have

$$(R(a_1, \ldots, a_n))^{\wedge} = R \circ (\hat{a}_1, \ldots, \hat{a}_n)$$

whence it follows that if A has no radical, $R(a_1, \ldots, a_n)$ only depends on the values assumed by R on $\mathrm{sp}(a_1, \ldots, a_n)$.

Similarly as in the case of one variable we are going to give a meaning to $f(a_1, \ldots, a_n)$ for more general functions f, namely for the functions which are holomorphic in the neighbourhood of $\mathrm{sp}(a_1, \ldots, a_n)$; we can construct $f(a_1, \ldots, a_n)$ by using the Cauchy integral formula with several variables, but great difficulties arise as soon as we try to determine the manifold on which we integrate; we will use here a method introduced by L. Waelbroeck, based on exterior differential calculus; we will now give some idea of it in the case of one variable: take the formula

$$f(a) = {}^{1}/_{(2\pi i)} \cdot \int_{\Gamma} f(z) \cdot (ze - a)^{-1}\, \mathrm{d}z;$$

let V be the relatively compact open set with boundary Γ and let φ be an indefinitely differentiable function (as a function of two real variables) with compact support contained in V and equal to 1 in the neighbourhood of $\mathrm{sp}\, a$; we set

$$u(z) = \begin{cases} (1 - \varphi(z))\,(ze - a)^{-1} & \text{if} \quad z \in \mathfrak{C} - \mathrm{sp}\, a \\ 0 & \text{if} \quad z \in \mathrm{sp}\, a; \end{cases}$$

then

$$f(a) = {}^1/_{(2\pi i)} \cdot \int_\Gamma f(z)\, u(z)\, \mathrm{d}z = {}^1/_{(2\pi i)} \cdot \int_V (f(z)\, \mathrm{d}u \wedge \mathrm{d}z + u(z)\, \mathrm{d}f \wedge \mathrm{d}z)$$

from Stokes' formula; but the second term is zero since f is holomorphic on V and finally

$$f(a) = {}^1/_{(2\pi i)} \cdot \int_V f(z)\, \mathrm{d}u \wedge \mathrm{d}z.$$

The element $f(a_1, \ldots, a_n)$ will temporarily be denoted $T_{a_1, \ldots, a_n}(\tilde{f})$ and it will be understood that in this notation $\tilde{f}$ always denotes *the germ of f in the neighbourhood of* $\mathrm{sp}(a_1, \ldots, a_n)$.

§ 4.2. *Statement of the theorems*

Theorem 4.1. For any sequence $(a_1, \ldots, a_n)$ of elements of A there is a continuous morphism $T_{a_1, \ldots, a_n}$ of $\mathcal{O}(\mathrm{sp}(a_1, \ldots, a_n))$ into A transforming the germ of the function 1 into e, that of the function $(z_1, \ldots, z_n) \to z_i$ into a_i $(i = 1, \ldots, n)$ and satisfying the following condition.

(α) if $p \leqq n$ and if f and g are functions holomorphic respectively in the neighbourhoods of $\mathrm{sp}(a_1, \ldots, a_n)$ and of $\mathrm{sp}(a_1, \ldots, a_p)$, satisfying $f(z_1, \ldots, z_n) = g(z_1, \ldots, z_p)$, then $T_{a_1, \ldots, a_n}(\tilde{f}) = T_{a_1, \ldots, a_p}(\tilde{g})$.

The family $(T_{a_1, \ldots, a_n})$ is uniquely determined. Moreover, the morphisms $T_{a_1, \ldots, a_n}$ have the following properties:

(i) if f is a rational function regular on $\mathrm{sp}(a_1, \ldots, a_n)$, we have $T_{a_1, \ldots, a_n}(\tilde{f}) = f(a_1, \ldots, a_n)$;

(ii) if A is the field of complex numbers, we have $T_{a_1, \ldots, a_n}(\tilde{f}) = f(a_1, \ldots, a_n)$.

(iii) if L is a continuous morphism of A into a commutative Banach algebra with unit B, transforming the unit element of A into that of B, we have $L(T_{a_1, \ldots, a_n}(\tilde{f})) = T_{La_1, \ldots, La_n}(\tilde{f})$ for any function f holomorphic in the neighbourhood of $\mathrm{sp}(a_1, \ldots, a_n)$;

(iv) $(T_{a_1, \ldots, a_n}(\tilde{f}))\hat{} = f \circ (\hat{a}_1, \ldots, \hat{a}_n)$;

(v) $\mathrm{sp}(T_{a_1, \ldots, a_n}(\tilde{f})) = f(\mathrm{sp}(a_1, \ldots, a_n))$;

(vi) let $f_1, \ldots, f_p$ be functions holomorphic in the neighbourhood of $\mathrm{sp}(a_1, \ldots, a_n)$, $b_i = T_{a_1, \ldots, a_n}(\tilde{f}_i)$ $(i = 1, \ldots, p)$, f the mapping $(f_1,$

$\ldots, f_p)$ of $\mathfrak{C}^n$ into $\mathfrak{C}^p$; we have $\mathrm{sp}(b_1, \ldots, b_p) = f(\mathrm{sp}(a_1, \ldots, a_n))$ and if g is a function holomorphic in the neighbourhood of $\mathrm{sp}(b_1, \ldots, b_p)$, we have $T_{b_1,\ldots,b_p}(\tilde{g}) = T_{a_1,\ldots,a_n}(\widetilde{g \circ f})$.

Theorem 4.2. (Runge-Weil-Oka). If X is a polynomially compact subset of $\mathfrak{C}^n$, the germs of the polynomial functions in the neighbourhood of X are everywhere dense in $\mathcal{O}(X)$.

§ 4.3. *Proof of existence (beginning)*

We will often write a instead of $(a_1, \ldots, a_n)$ and z instead of $(z_1, \ldots, z_n)$.

a) First we show that there exist mappings $v_1, \ldots, v_n$ from $\mathfrak{C}^n$ − sp a into A which are indefinitely differentiable (as functions of 2n real variables) and satisfy identically

$$\sum_{i=1}^{n} (z_i e - a_i) \cdot v_i(z) = e. \tag{1}$$

For any $z \in \mathscr{C}^n$ − sp a we know that there exist elements $w_1(z), \ldots, w_n(z)$ of A satisfying

$$\sum_{i=1}^{n} (z_i e - a_i) \cdot w_i(z) = e;$$

the functions w_i need not be indefinitely differentiable, but can be regularized so that they are; for z' sufficiently close of z, say for $z' \in V_z$, an open neighbourhood of z, $\sum (z'_i e - a_i) \cdot w_i(z)$ is invertible; we then set

$$v_i(z, z') = w_i(z) \cdot (\sum_j (z'_j e - a_j) \cdot w_j(z))^{-1};$$

the mappings $z' \to v_i(z, z')$ are indefinitely differentiable and satisfy (1), which hence has a local solution; we deduce a global solution by using an indefinitely differentiable partition of unity subject to the open covering (V_z) of $\mathfrak{C}^n$ − sp a, i.e. a family (λ_α) of positive real functions on $\mathfrak{C}^n$ − sp a, which are indefinitely differentiable and have the following properties:

– each point of $\mathfrak{C}^n$ − sp a has a neighbourhood on which the λ_α are identically zero except for a finite number of them

– for any α there is a $z_\alpha \in \mathfrak{C}^n - \operatorname{sp} a$ such that V_{z_α} contains the support of λ_α

– $\sum \lambda_\alpha = 1$.

We obtain a solution of the problem by taking

$$v_i(z) = \sum_\alpha \lambda_\alpha(z) \cdot v_i(z_\alpha, z).$$

b) Let us now prove the following: for any open neighbourhood U of sp a there exist.

– a complex function φ on $\mathfrak{C}^n$, which is indefinitely differentiable, with compact support contained in U and equal to 1 in the neighbourhood of sp a;

– mappings $u_1, \ldots, u_n$ of $\mathfrak{C}^n$ into A, which are indefinitely differentiable and zero on sp a

which satisfy identically

$$\sum_i (z_i e - a_i) \cdot u_i(z) = (1 - \varphi(z))e. \tag{2}$$

It suffices in fact to take φ as shown and to set

$$u_i(z) = \begin{cases} (1 - \varphi(z)) \cdot v_i(z) & \text{if} \quad z \in \mathfrak{C}^n - \operatorname{sp} a \\ 0 & \text{if} \quad z \in \operatorname{sp} a. \end{cases}$$

c) given U and $\varphi, u_1, \ldots, u_n$ being chosen as above, the differential form $\omega = du_1 \wedge \ldots \wedge du_n \wedge dz_1 \wedge \ldots \wedge dz_n$ has a compact support contained in that of φ.

Indeed, if we place ourselves on the outside of φ and differentiate (2);

$$\sum_i u_i \, dz_i + \sum_i (z_i e - a_i) \, du_i = 0;$$

multiplying to the right by $\sum_j (-1)^{j-1} u_j du_1 \wedge \ldots d\hat{u}_j \wedge \ldots du_n \wedge dz_1 \wedge \ldots dz_n$ we obtain $\omega = 0$.

d) let us also take a function f holomorphic on U; the expression $n!/(2\pi i)^n \int_U f\omega$ is meaningful thanks to c). We will see that its value does not depend on the choice of $\varphi, u_1, \ldots, u_n$ (satisfying (2), naturally). Hence let $\varphi', u_1', \ldots, u_1'$ be another choice; we will show that $f(du_1' \wedge \ldots \wedge du_n' - du_1 \wedge \ldots \wedge du_n) \wedge dz_1 \wedge \ldots \wedge dz_n$ is the differential of a form τ with compact support K contained in U; then taking a compact set K', $K \subset K' \subset U$, with a sufficiently regular boundary $\tilde{f} K'$, we will have

$$\int_U f(du_1' \wedge \ldots \wedge du_n' - du_1 \wedge \ldots \wedge du_n) \wedge dz_1 \wedge \ldots \wedge dz_n = \int_{K'} d\tau$$
$$= \int_{\tilde{f} K'} \tau = 0.$$

We have

$$u_i' - u_i = u_i' \left(\sum_j (z_j e - a_j) u_j + \varphi e\right) - u_i \left(\sum_j (z_j e - a_j) u_j' + \varphi' e\right)$$
$$= \sum_j (z_j e - a_j) \alpha_{i,j} + \beta_i$$

where we have set

$$\alpha_{i,j} = u_i' u_j - u_i u_j'$$
$$\beta_i = u_i' \varphi - u_i \varphi';$$

we obviously have $\alpha_{i,j} + \alpha_{j,i} = 0$ and β_i has a compact support contained in U; we go from $(u_1, \ldots, u_n)$ to $(u_1', \ldots, u_n')$ by a series of transformations of the form

$$u_1' = u_1 + (z_2 e - a_2) \alpha_{1,2}$$
$$u_2' = u_2 - (z_1 e - a_1) \alpha_{1,2}$$
$$u_3' = u_3, \ldots, u_n' = u_n$$

or of the form

$$u_1' = u_1 + \beta_1$$
$$u_2' = u_2, \ldots, u_n' = u_n$$

and it suffices to prove the assertion in each of these two cases; in the first case we can take

$$\tau = f\varphi \, d\alpha_{1,2} \wedge du_3 \wedge \ldots \wedge du_n \wedge dz_1 \wedge \ldots \wedge dz_n$$

and in the second

$$\tau = f\beta_1 \, du_2 \wedge \ldots \wedge du_n \wedge dz_1 \wedge \ldots \wedge dz_n.$$

e) From what we are after seing, $n!/(2\pi i)^n \int_U f\omega$ depends only on U and on f; we can hence set

$$S_{a,U}(f) = n!/(2\pi i)^n \int_U f\omega$$

and $S_{a,U}$ is a mapping of $\mathcal{O}(U)$ into A which is obviously linear and continuous. But infact $S_{a,U}$ only depends on the germ of f in the neighbourhood of sp a; because, let f' be holomorphic on another open neighbourhood U' of sp a, where f and f' are equal on a third neighbourhood $U'' \subset U \cap U'$; take φ with compact support contained in U''; a differential form ω corresponds to it and we get

$$S_{a,U}(f) = n!/(2\pi i)^n \int_{U''} f\omega = n!/(2\pi i)^n \int_{U''} f'\omega = S_{a,U'}(f').$$

The various mappings $S_{a,U}$ define thus a continuous linear mapping, which we will denote by $T_{a_1,\ldots,a_n}$ or T_a, of $\mathcal{O}(\text{sp } a)$ into A.

f) We now prove the following: if $a_1, \ldots, a_n, a'_1, \ldots, a'_p$ are elements of A, f and f' are functions holomorphic in the neighbourhood of sp a and sp a', respectively, and F is the function holomorphic in the neighbourhood of sp(a, a') defined by

$$F(z, z') = f(z) \cdot f'(z'),$$

we get

$$T_{a,a'}(\tilde{F}) = T_a(\tilde{f}) \cdot T_{a'}(\tilde{f}').$$

Suppose f and f' are defined respectively on U and U' and let $\varphi, u_1, \ldots, u_n$ (resp. $\varphi', u'_1, \ldots, u'_p$) be elements chosen as described in b) with respect to $a_1, \ldots, a_n, U$ (resp. $a'_1, \ldots, a'_p, U'$); for the elements associated with $a_1, \ldots, a_n, a'_1, \ldots, a'_p, U \times U'$ we can take $\varphi'', u''_1, \ldots, u''_{n+p}$ defined by

$$\varphi''(z, z') = \varphi(z) \cdot \varphi'(z')$$

$$u''_i(z, z') = \begin{cases} u_i(z) & \text{for } i = 1, \ldots, n \\ \varphi(z) \cdot u'_{i-n}(z') & \text{for } i = n+1, \ldots, n+p \end{cases}$$

and we must show that

$$(n+p)! \int_{U \times U} f(z)f'(z')\, du_1 \wedge \ldots du_n \wedge d(\varphi u'_1) \wedge \ldots d(\varphi u'_p) \wedge dz_1 \wedge \ldots dz_n \wedge dz'_1 \wedge \ldots dz'_p$$

$$- n!p! \int_{U \times U'} f(z)f'(z')\, du_1 \wedge \ldots du_n \wedge du'_1 \wedge \ldots du'_p \wedge dz_1 \wedge \ldots dz_n \wedge dz'_1 \wedge \ldots dz'_p = 0.$$

The first part of the first member is equal to

$$(n+p)! \int_{U\times U'} f(z)f'(z')\,\varphi(z)^p\, du_1 \wedge \ldots du_n \wedge du'_1 \wedge \ldots du'_p \wedge dz_1 \wedge \ldots dz_n \wedge dz'_1 \wedge \ldots dz'_p$$

plus terms which are zero since they are of degree $> 2n$ with respect to the $2n$ real variables $\mathcal{R}z_1, \ldots, \mathcal{R}z_n, \mathcal{I}z_1, \ldots, \mathcal{I}z_n$; the first member is thus the integral of the differential form

$$((n+p)!\,\varphi^p - n!\,p!)ff'\, du_1 \wedge \ldots du_n \wedge du'_1 \wedge \ldots du'_p \wedge dz_1 \wedge \ldots dz_n \wedge dz'_1 \wedge \ldots dz'_p$$

and it is zero since the latter is the differential of the form

$$p!\,ff' \sum_{i=1}^{n} \sum_{j=1}^{p} \frac{(n+j-1)!}{j!} \varphi^j (-1)^{i-1} u_i du_1 \wedge \ldots \widehat{du_i} \wedge \ldots du_n \wedge du'_1 \wedge \ldots du'_p \wedge dz_1 \wedge \ldots dz_n \wedge dz'_1 \wedge \ldots dz'_p$$

which has a compact support contained in $U \times U'$.

g) From f) we see by recurrence on n that $T_{a_1,\ldots,a_n}$ transforms the germ of the function 1 into e and that of the function $z \to z_i$ into a_i; condition (α) is then trivially verified.

h) If f is a polynomial we have $T_{a_1,\ldots,a_n}(\tilde{f}) = f(a_1, \ldots, a_n)$. Indeed, because of the linearity of $T_{a_1,\ldots,a_n}$, it suffices to show this is true for monomials, and it is true for monomials as can be seen by repeated application of f).

§ 4.4. *Proof of properties* (ii), (iii) *and* (iv)

(ii) If A is the field of complex numbers, $\mathrm{sp}(a_1, \ldots, a_n) = \{(a_1, \ldots, a_n)\}$; the assertion is true if f is a polynomial, by virtue of § 3, h); in the general case, f is the sum of a uniformly convergent series on the neighbourhood U of $(a_1, \ldots, a_n)$, hence a uniform limit on U (and a fortiori a limit in the sense of $\mathcal{O}(\{(a_1, \ldots, a_n)\})$) of polynomials; the assertion follows thus from the continuity of T_a established in § 3, e).

(iii) If f is holomorphic on $U \supset \mathrm{sp}\, a$ and if $\varphi, u_1, \ldots, u_n$ are chosen as described in § 3, b), the functions $\varphi, L \circ u_1, \ldots, L \circ u_n$ have the same properties with respect to $La_1, \ldots, La_n$ and we have

$$L(T_{a_1,\ldots,a_n}(\tilde{f})) = n!/(2\pi i)^n L\left(\int_U f\, du_1 \wedge \ldots du_n \wedge dz_1 \wedge \ldots dz_n\right)$$

$$= n!/(2\pi i)^n \int_U f d(L \circ u_1) \wedge \ldots d(L \circ u_n) \wedge dz_1 \wedge \ldots dz_n$$

$$= T_{La_1,\ldots,La_n}(\tilde{f}).$$

(iv) We must prove that for any character χ we have

$$\chi(T_{a_1,\ldots,a_n}(\tilde{f})) = f(\chi(a_1), \ldots, \chi(a_n))$$

and this follows from (ii) and (iii).

§ 4.5. *Proof of Theorem* 4.2.

Let X be a polynomially convex compact subset of $\mathfrak{C}^n$ and let f be a holomorphic function on an open neighbourhood U of X; we know (cf. Appendix I) that U contains a polynomially convex compact neighbourhood V of X; on the other hand, from proposition 2.11, V is the spectrum of a Banach algebra B with n generators $a_1, \ldots, a_n$; we can construct $T_{a_1,\ldots,a_n}(\tilde{f})$ and we have (property (iv))

$$(T_{a_1,\ldots,a_n}(\tilde{f}))^\frown = f/V;$$

f is hence a limit of polynomials uniformly on V and a fortiori in the $\mathcal{O}(X)$ sense.

§ 4.6. *Proof of existence (end)*

There remains to establish the multiplicativity of $T_{a_1,\ldots,a_n}$. Hence let f and g be holomorphic on $U \supset \mathrm{sp}(a_1, \ldots, a_n)$; introduce the elements $a_{n+1}, \ldots, a_{n+p}$ of Lemma 2.2 as well as the notation A'; we write $\mathfrak{C}^{n+p} = \mathfrak{C}^n \times \mathfrak{C}^p$ and denote by u the projection mapping of

$\mathfrak{C}^{n+p}$ onto $\mathfrak{C}^n$; $f \circ u$, $g \circ u$ and $fg \circ u$ are holomorphic in the neighbourhood of $\mathrm{sp}_A(a_1, \ldots, a_{n+p})$ and we have, by virtue of the condition (α);

$$T_{a_1, \ldots, a_{n+p}}(\widetilde{f \circ u}) = T_{a_1, \ldots, a_n}(\tilde{f}) \tag{3}$$

$$T_{a_1, \ldots, a_{n+p}}(\widetilde{g \circ u}) = T_{a_1, \ldots, a_n}(\tilde{g}) \tag{4}$$

$$T_{a_1, \ldots, a_{n+p}}(\widetilde{fg \circ u}) = T_{a_1, \ldots, a_n}(\widetilde{fg}); \tag{5}$$

but since $\mathrm{sp}_{A'}(a_1, \ldots, a_{n+p})$ is polynomially convex (Proposition 2.10), it follows from Theorem 4.2 that the germs of $f \circ u$ and $g \circ u$ in the neighbourhood of $\mathrm{sp}_{A'}(a_1, \ldots, a_{n+p})$, and a fortiori the germs in the neighbourhood of $\mathrm{sp}_A(a_1, \ldots, a_{n+p})$, are limits of germs of polynomial functions; for such functions the first member of (5) is equal to the product of the first members of (3) and (4) (cf. §4.3, h)); the property follows thus from the continuity of $T_{a_1, \ldots, a_{n+p}}$.

§ 4.7. *Proof of uniqueness and of properties* (i), (v) *and* (vi)

Uniqueness. Suppose we have constructed two families of morphisms $(T_{a_1, \ldots, a_n})$ and $(T'_{a_1, \ldots, a_n})$ satisfying the required conditions; let $a_1, \ldots, a_n \in A$ and let f be holomorphic on $U \supset \mathrm{sp}(a_1, \ldots, a_n)$; with the notations of § 6, we get

$$T_{a_1, \ldots, a_{n+p}}(\widetilde{f \circ u}) = T_{a_1, \ldots, a_n}(\tilde{f})$$

$$T'_{a_1, \ldots, a_{n+p}}(\widetilde{f \circ u}) = T'_{a_1, \ldots, a_n}(\tilde{f})$$

and the reasoning proceeds as in § 6.

Property (i). Follows immediately fron the fact that $T_{a_1, \ldots, a_n}$ is a morphism, transforming the germ of the function 1 into e and that of the function $z \to z_i$ into a_i.

(v) is an immediate consequence of (iv).

(vi): the first assertion follows trivially from (iv); to prove the second let

$$h(z', z) = g(z') - g(f(z));$$

h is holomorphic in the neighbourhood of $\mathrm{sp}(b_1, \ldots, b_p, a_1, \ldots, a_n)$ and since

$$T_{b,a}(\tilde{h}) = T_b(\tilde{g}) - T_a(\widetilde{g \circ f})$$

we must prove that $T_{b,a}(\tilde{h}) = 0$; now we have

$$h(z', z) = \sum_{i=1}^{p} (z'_i - f_i(z)) \cdot k_i(z', z)$$

where we have set

$$k_i(z', z) = \frac{g(z'_1, \ldots, z'_i, f_{i+1}(z), \ldots, f_p(z)) - g(z'_1, \ldots, z'_{i-1}, f_i(z), \ldots, f_p(z))}{z'_i - f_i(z)}$$

then

$$T_{b,a}(\tilde{h}) = \sum_{i=1}^{p} (b_i - T_a(\tilde{f}_i)) \cdot T_{b,a}(\tilde{k}_i) = 0 .$$

(For the holomorphy of k_i, see for instance [10], Theorem 4.6.)

§ 4.8. *Miscellaneous remarks*

Remark 4.1. If we restrict ourselves to algebras without radical, we can omit in the statement the theorem 4.2 and the condition (α), on condition that we add the property (iv) which replaces them advantageously in the proofs of the multiplicativity and of the uniqueness; moreover, it occurs for each individual morphism $T_{a_1, \ldots, a_n}$.

Remark 4.2. In passing we have proved the following: if a polynomially convex compact subset K of $\mathfrak{C}^n$ contains $\operatorname{sp}(a_1, \ldots, a_n)$, there is a unique continuous morphism of $\mathcal{O}(K)$ into A transforming the germ of the function 1 into e and that of the function $z \to z_i$ into a_i.

Remark 4.3. Suppose f is the sum of a power series $\sum c_{i_1, \ldots, i_n} z_1^{i_1} \ldots z_n^{i_n}$ which is uniformly convergent on a neighbourhood of $\operatorname{sp}(a_1, \ldots, a_n)$; then $T_{a_1, \ldots, a_n}(\tilde{f})$ is the sum of the commutatively convergent series $\sum c_{i_1, \ldots, i_n} a_1^{i_1} \ldots a_{i_n}^{n}$.

Remark 4.4. The notation $f(a_1, \ldots, a_n)$ is often used instead of $T_{a_1, \ldots, a_n}(\tilde{f})$.

Remark 4.5. The following result can be proved in the same way as Theorem 4.2: if X is a rationally convex compact subset of $\mathfrak{C}^n$, the germs of rational functions which are regular on X are everywhere dense in $\mathcal{O}(X)$.

Remark 4.6. Holomorphic functional calculus can be extended to the case of an infinity of variables.

§ 4.9. *Applications*

Holomorphic functional calculus with several variables is used to solve analytic functional equations; we will examine such a problem: finding idempotent elements.

Proposition 4.1. Let A be a C. B. A. with unit; if U is an open and closed subset of $\hat{A}$, there exists an idempotent element j of A such that $\hat{j}$ is the characteristic function of U.

We first prove the following: there exist elements $a_1, \ldots, a_n$ of A such that, denoting by p the mapping $\chi \to (\chi(a_1), \ldots, \chi(a_n))$ of $\hat{A}$ onto $\mathrm{sp}(a_1, \ldots, a_n)$, we have $p(U) \cap p(\hat{A} - U) = \varnothing$.

For all $x_1 \in U$ and all $x_2 \in \hat{A} - U$ there exists an element a_{x_1,x_2} such that $x_1(a_{x_1,x_2}) \neq x_2(a_{x_1,x_2})$; then there exist open neighbourhoods V_{x_1,x_2} and W_{x_1,x_2} of x_1 and x_2 such that

$$x_1' \in V_{x_1,x_2} \text{ and } x_2' \in W_{x_1,x_2} \Rightarrow x_1'(a_{x_1,x_2}) \neq x_2'(a_{x_1,x_2});$$

the open cover $(V_{x_1,x_2} \times W_{x_1,x_2})$ of $U \times (\hat{A} - U)$ contains a finite subcovering $(V_{x_{1,i}, x_{2,i}} \times W_{x_{1,i}, x_{2,i}})$ where $i = 1, \ldots, n$; the elements $a_{x_{1,i}, x_{2,i}}$ are the required elements since if $x_1 \in U$ and $x_2 \in \hat{A} - U$, (x_1, x_2) belongs to an open set $V_{x_{1,i}, x_{2,i}} \times W_{x_{1,i}, x_{2,i}}$ and then

$$x_1(a_{x_{1,i}, x_{2,i}}) \neq x_2(a_{x_{1,i}, x_{2,i}}).$$

Having established this, let f be a function holomorphic in the neighbourhood of $\mathrm{sp}(a_1, \ldots, a_n)$, equal to 1 on $p(U)$ and to 0 on $p(\hat{A} - U)$; let us set $j_0 = f(a_1, \ldots, a_n)$; $\hat{j}_0$ is equal to the characteristic function and j_0 is idempotent since $T_{a_1} \ldots T_{a_n}$ is a morphism of algebras.

Corollary 4.1. U is open and closed for the hk-topology.

Corollary 4.2. Any decomposition of $\hat{A}$ into the topological sum of two subspaces corresponds to a decomposition of A into a direct sum of two closed ideals (cf. Proposition 2.7).

A is indeed the direct sum of the closed ideals j. A and $(e - j) \cdot A$.

Corollary 4.3. If A is without radical and $\hat{A}$ is finite, A is algebraically isomorphic to the direct sum of a finite number of algebras isomorphic to $\mathfrak{C}$.

Theorem 4.3. A commutative Banach algebra without radical whose spectrum is compact admits a unit element.

Indeed, $\hat{A}$ is then open and closed in $\hat{\tilde{A}}$; let $j \in \tilde{A}$ be idempotent, such that $\hat{j}$ is the characteristic function of $\hat{A}$; we obviously have $j \in A$ and on the other hand for all $x \in A$ we have $jx = x$ since $\hat{j}\hat{x} = \hat{x}$.

Remark 4.7. The preceding result is false if we do not suppose that A is without radical, as can be seen by considering the direct sum of a C. B. A. with unit and of a C. B. A. without unit and with an empty spectrum.

Exercise. If X is a connected topological space and A is a Banach subalgebra of $\mathscr{C}^\infty(X)$ containing 1, then $\hat{A}$ is connected.

§ 4.10. *Complements: applications to functional calculus with one variable*

1. *Taylor's formula.* Let be $a \in A$, $\alpha > 0$, U the set of complex numbers whose distance from sp a is $< \alpha$, $b \in A$, such that $\nu(b) < \alpha/4$, $f \subset \mathcal{O}(U)$; then $\mathrm{sp}(a + b) \subset U$ and we have

$$f(a + b) = \sum_0^\infty 1/n! \cdot f^{(n)}(a) \cdot b^n.$$

Sketch of the proof: sp(a, b), is contained in the open set V composed of the couples (z, z') satisfying

$$\begin{cases} \text{distance from } z \text{ to sp } a < \alpha/4 \\ |z'| < \alpha/4; \end{cases}$$

the function of two variables $g(z, z') = f(z + z')$ is holomorphic on V and is the sum of the uniformly convergent series $\sum 1/n! \cdot f^{(n)}(z) \cdot z'^n$; hence

$$f(a + b) = g(a, b) = \sum 1/n! \cdot f^{(n)}(a) \cdot b^n.$$

2. *Properties of the mapping* $a \to f(a)$.

Let U be am open subset of $\mathfrak{C}$ and E the open set (cf. § 1.5, exercise) composed of the a such that sp $a \subset U$; for all $f \in \mathcal{O}(U)$ we can consider the mapping $a \to f(a)$ of E into A; it is *analytic* in the following sense:

$$\lim_{b \to 0} \|f(a + b) - f(a) - b \cdot f'(a)\| \,/\, \|b\| = 0$$

(this follows from Taylor's formula and we see that $f'(a)$ plays the role of the deriviative); it extends the mapping $ze \to f(z)e$ of $U \cdot e$ into $\mathfrak{C} \cdot e$; one shows that these two properties characterize it --- at least in the connected components of E which meet $U \cdot e$ (cf. [15], 5.17).

Exercises

1. For any z such that $|z-1| < 1$ we set $\log z = \log |z| + i \arg z$ with $-\pi/2 < \arg z < \pi/2$; show that if sp a and sp b are contained in the set defined by $|z-1| < {}^1/_4$, we have

$$\log ab = \log a + \log b.$$

[Use the function of two variables $\log zz'$.]

2. Let u be a continuous mapping of $\mathfrak{R}_+$ into A satisfying

$$u(s+t) = u(s) \cdot u(t) \quad \text{and} \quad u(0) = e;$$

show that there exists an $a \in A$ such that $u(s) = \exp s\, a$ for all s; generalize to the case where we no longer suppose $u(0) = e$.

[Use the preceding exercise.]

This result should be compared with the study in § 8.2, no. 4.

3. Establish Taylor's formula in the case of several variables.

CHAPTER V

REGULAR ALGEBRAS

§ 5.1. *Definitions and basic properties*

First definition. A commutative Banach algebra A is said to be *regular* if the topology of simple convergence and the hk-topology are are identical on $\hat{A}$.

This is equivalent to saying that for any closed subset F of $\hat{A}$ (for the topology of simple convergence) we have $h(k(F)) = F$ or again $\chi \notin F$ implies $\chi \notin h(k(F))$, whence the

Second definition. A commutative Banach algebra A is said to be *regular* if for any closed (in the sense of the topology of simple convergence) subset F of $\hat{A}$ and any point $\chi \notin F$ there exists an $x \in A$ such that $\hat{x}$ is zero on F and non-zero at χ.

For a regular C. B. A., the Šilov boundary obviously coincides with the spectrum; any closed subset $F \subset \hat{A}$ is canonically homeomorphic to the spectrumof $A/k(F)$; any open subset $U \subset \hat{A}$ is canonically homeomorphic to the spectrum of $k(\hat{A} - U)$ (cf. Propositions 2.5 and 2.6).

Examples. The algebras in examples (a), (b), (c), (e), (f), (g) are regular: for (b) and (c) this is trivial; for (e) it is readily proved; for (a) and (g) see § 7.4; for (f), it is proved in Harmonic Analysis. The algebra in example (d) is obviously not regular.

Proposition 5.1. Let A be a regular C. B. A., I an ideal of A, F_1 a closed subset and F_2 a compact subset of $\hat{A}$ such that $(h(I) \cup F_1) \cap F_2 = \varnothing$; there exists an element x of I such that $\hat{x}$ is equal to 0 on F_1 and to 1 on F_2.

Take $I_1 = k(F_1)$ and $I_2 = k(F_2)$; A/I_2 is without radical and since its spectrum is homeomorphic to F_2, it admits a unit element e (cf. Theorem 4.3); we denote by P the canonical homorphism $A \to A/I_2$; we have

$$h(I) \cup F_1 = h(I) \cup h(I_1) = h(I \cap I_1) \qquad \text{(cf. § 2.4)}$$

$$F_2 = h(I_2)$$

hence no character of A can vanish on both I_2 and on $I \cap I_1$, or again, no character of A/I_2 can vanish on $P(I \cap I_1)$; it follows that that $e \in P(I \cap I_1)$; any element x of $I \cap I_1$ such that $P(x) = e$ will satisfy the required conditions. Q. E. D.

We can deduce the following property, which is in a sense a "normality" property:

Corollary 5.1. If A is a regular C. B. A., F_1 a closed subset and F_2 a compact subset of $\hat{A}$, and F_1 and F_2 are disjoint, then there exists an element x of A such that $\hat{x}$ is equal to 0 on F_1 and to 1 on F_2.

Corollary 5.2. If I is an ideal of A and F a compact subset of $\hat{A}$ disjoint from $h(I)$, there exists an element x of I such that $\hat{x}$ is equal to 1 on F.

Proposition 5.2. Let A be a regular C. B. A. without radical and F a closed subset of $\hat{A}$; among the ideals I of A such that $h(I) = F$, there is a largest one, namely $k(F)$, and a smallest one: the set of x such that the support of x is compact and disjoint from F.

First we have $h(k(F)) = F$ and if $h(I) = F$, $I \subset k(h(I)) = k(F)$; whence the first assertion.

We then denote by J the second ideal considered in the statement; we obviously have $h(J) \supset F$; then if $\chi \notin F$ there exist a compact neighbourhood V of χ, disjoint from F, and an element x of A such that $\hat{x}$ vanishes outside V and does not vanish at χ; then $x \in J$ and $\chi \notin h(J)$; this proves that $h(J) = F$. It remains to be shown that $h(I) = F \Rightarrow I \supset J$; let $x \in J$; there exists a $y \in I$ such that $\hat{y}$ is equal to 1 on the support of $\hat{x}$; then $\hat{x}\hat{y} = \hat{x}$ and since A is without radical $xy = x$ and $x \in I$.

Corollary 5.3. (Abstract form of Wiener's tauberian theorem). Let A be a regular C. B. A. without radical and with the following property: the ideal of the x such that $\hat{x}$ has compact support is everywhere dense in A; then every closed ideal of A is contained in at least one regular maximal ideal.

Indeed, if an ideal I is not contained in any regular maximal ideal, $h(I) = \varnothing$ and hence I contains all the x such that $\hat{x}$ has compact support.

Exercises

1. Let X be a non-compact locally compact space; the set $\mathscr{K}(X)$ of continuous functions with compact supports is the smallest dense ideal of $\mathscr{C}_0(X)$,

2. Every closed ideal and every quotient (but not every closed subalgebra!) of a regular C. B. A. is regular; the direct sum and the tensor product of two regular C. B. A. are regular.

§ 5.2. *Localization theorem*

Definition. Let A be a C. B. A. and χ an element of $\hat{A}$; a complex function f on $\hat{A}$ is said to *belong to* $\mathscr{F}A$ locally at χ if it coincides on the neighbourhood of χ with a function $\hat{x}$, $x \in A$.

Analogous definition for local membership of $\mathscr{F}B$ where B is a subalgebra of A. All this holds, mutatis mutandis, for the point at infinity of $\hat{A}$.

Theorem 5.1. If A is regular and if I is an ideal of A, any function f which belongs locally to $\mathscr{F}I$ at each point of A, including the point at infinity, belongs to $\mathscr{F}I$ (in other words it is the Gelfand transform of an element of I).

The hypothesis made on the point at infinity allows us to consider only the case where A is unitary, hence $\hat{A}$ is compact; then there exist elements $x_1, \ldots, x_n$ of I and an open covering $U_1, \ldots, U_n$ of $\hat{A}$ such that $f \mid U_i = x_i \mid U_i$; then an open covering V_i such that $\overline{V}_i \subset U_i$; it suffices then to prove the following (the sequel being merely a repetition of it): there exists a $y \in I$ such that f and $\hat{y}$ coincide on $U_1 \cup V_2$; now there exists a $u \in A$ such that $\hat{u}$ is equal to 1 on $\overline{V}_2$ and to 0 outside U_2; we can take $y = ux_2 + (e - u)x_1$.

Corollary 5.4. If A is regular, every function which belongs locally to $\mathscr{F}A$ at each point of $\hat{A}$ including the point at infinity, belongs to $\mathscr{F}A$.

The corollary 5.4 allows us to improve holomorphic functional calculus in the following manner:

Proposition 5.3. Let A be a regular C. B. A. with unit and f a complex function on $\hat{A}$ with the following property: for all $\chi_0 \in \hat{A}$ there exist an open neighbourhood U of χ_0, an element x of A and a function φ holomorphic in the neighbourhood of the set of $\hat{x}(\chi)$ where $\chi \in U$, satisfying

$$f(\chi) = \varphi(\hat{x}(\chi)) \qquad \forall \chi \in U;$$

then $f \in \mathcal{F}A$.

It suffices to find for all χ_0 an element y of A such that $\hat{y}$ coincides with f in the neighbourhood of χ_0. Let V be a neighbourhood of χ_0 such that $\overline{V} \subset U$; let $\dot{x}$ be the canonical image of x in $A/k(V)$; φ is holomorphic in the neighbourhood of sp $\dot{x}$; we can hence consider $\varphi(\dot{x})$ and we have $\widehat{\varphi(\dot{x})}(\chi) = f(\chi)$ for $\chi \in V$; it suffices to take y such that $\dot{y} = \varphi(\dot{x})$.

Example. This allows us to solve certain equations in A, for instance $x^2 = a$, assuming $\hat{a}$ does not vanish and admits a square root in $\mathcal{C}(\hat{A})$; because, if f is this square root, in the neighbourhood of each point χ_0, $f(\chi)$ is the sum of a power series in $\hat{a}(\chi) - \hat{a}(\chi_0)$; then there exists a $y \in A$ such that $\hat{y} = f$ and the problem is solved – – – at least if A is without radical.

Complements. Let A be a regular or non-regular unitary C. B. A.; the closure in $\mathcal{C}(\hat{A})$ of the algebra of the functions belonging locally to $\mathcal{F}A$ at each point has spectrum $\hat{A}$ (cf. [37]). In [21] one will find sufficient conditions for the validity of Corollary 5.4; and in [30] an example of a non-regular algebra for which it does not hold.

Exercises

1. Let A be a regular C. B. A. and $(U_i)_{i=1,\ldots,n}$ an open covering of $\hat{A}$; there exists a sequence $(f_i)_{i=1,\ldots,n}$ of elements of $\mathcal{F}A$ satisfying

$$\begin{cases} f_i(\chi) = 0 \text{ for } \chi \in \hat{A} - U_i \\ \sum f_i(\chi) = 1 \text{ for all } \chi. \end{cases}$$

[Proceed by recurrence on n; note that (f_i) does not constitute a partition of unity in the sense of [6].]

2. Generalize Proposition 5.3. to the case of several variables.

§ 5.3. *Comparison of a closed ideal I and of $k(h(I))$*

Lemma 5.1. Let A be a regular C. B. A., x an element of A, I an ideal of A; x belongs locally to $\mathcal{F}I$ at each point χ belonging to $\hat{A} - h(I)$ or to the interior of $h(\{x\})$.

Because in the first case there exists (Corollary 5.2) a $u \in I$ such that $\hat{u} = 1$ in the neighbourhood of χ and we have $\hat{x} = \hat{u}\hat{x}$ in the neighbourhood of χ; in the second case $\hat{x}$ is zero in the neighbourhood of χ.

Proposition 5.4. (Šilov). Let A be a regular C. B. A. without radical and satisfying the following condition (the Ditkin condition)

(D) for all $\chi \in \hat{\hat{A}}$ and all $x \in \operatorname{Ker} \chi$ there exists a sequence $x_n \in A$ such that $xx_n \to x$ and that $\hat{x}_n$ is zero in the neighbourhood of χ;

on the other hand, let I be a closed ideal of A and x an element of $k(h(I))$; if (bdry $h(\{x\})) \cap h(I)$ contains no non-empty perfect subset, then $x \in I$.

(bdry denotes the topological boundary).

By virtue of Theorem 5.1 it suffices to show that the set E of χ for which $\hat{x}$ does not belong locally to $\mathcal{F}I$ is empty; now we have, because of Lemma 5.1, $E \subset h(I)$ and since $h(I) \subset h(\{x\})$, we have, again by Lemma 5.1, $E \subset$ bdry $h(\{x\})$, hence $E \subset$ (bdry $h(\{x\})) \cap h(I)$), moreover E is obviously closed; it remains to be proved that E has no isolated points.

Let χ_0 be an isolated point of E; there exists an open neighbourhood U of χ_0 such that $\bar{U} \cap E = \{\chi_0\}$; by virtue of the condition (D) there exists a sequence $y_n \in A$ such that $xy_n \to x$ and that y_n is zero in the neighbourhood of χ_0; let z be an element of $\tilde{A}$ such that $\hat{z}$ is equal to 1 in the neighbourhood of χ_0 and to 0 outside U (we note that χ_0 can be at infinity!); $\hat{x}\hat{y}_n\hat{z}$ belongs locally to $\mathcal{F}I$ at each point of $\hat{A}$, hence $xy_nz \in I$ and $xz \in I$; since $\hat{z} = 1$ in the neighbourhood of χ_0, $\hat{x}$ belongs locally to $\mathcal{F}I$ at χ_0, which gives a contradiction.

Corollary 5.5. If $h(I)$ contains no non-empty perfect subset, we have $I = k(h(I))$.

Corollary 5.6. If $h(I)$ is discrete we have $I = k(h(I))$.

§ 5.4. *Localization*

We will here draw some parallels with the algebraic theory of localization as well as with the theory of sheaves, without any idea of their real interest.

Let A be a regular C. B. A., χ a character of A, N_χ its kernel; denoting by

– A_χ the algebra of germs of functions $\hat{x}$ $(x \in A)$ in the neighbourhood of χ

– M_χ the ideal of A_χ formed by the germs of functions vanishing at χ

– T_χ the canonical homomorphism of A onto A_χ

– $P_\chi = T_\chi^{-1}(\{0\})$ = the set of x such that the support of $\hat{x}$ does not contain χ; in general it is a non-closed ideal

– Q_χ the ideal of A formed by the x such that the support of $\hat{x}$ is compact and does not contain χ; we have

$$Q_\chi \subset P_\chi \subset N_\chi = T_\chi^{-1}(M_\chi) \subset A\,.$$

The algebra A_χ contains the germ of the function 1 (Corollary 5.1) and hence it is *unitary*; on the other hand it is easy to see that M_χ is the set of non-invertible elements of A_χ (use a compact neighbourhood V of χ and the algebra $A/k(V)$); it follows that M_χ *if the largest ideal* of A_χ (under these conditions one says that A_χ is a *local ring*).

Let us now compare A_χ with what is denoted in algebra by A_N and called "local ring of A in N" – – – at least if A is unitary (cf. [5], no. 1); we recall that A_N is the quotient of $A \times (A - N)$ by the equivalence relation

$$(x, y) \sim (x', y') \Longleftrightarrow \exists\, z \in A - N : z(xy' - yx') = 0. \qquad (1)$$

For $(x, y) \in A \times (A - N)$, $T_\chi(y)$ is invertible and we can consider $T_\chi(x)\, T_\chi(y)^{-1}$; this only depends on the class of (x, y) with respect to $\sim$, since (1) implies that

$$T_\chi(z) \cdot (T_\chi(x) T_\chi(y') - T_\chi(y)\, T_\chi(x')) = 0$$

and, since $T_\chi(z)$ is invertible,

$$T_\chi(x)\, T_\chi(y') = T_\chi(y)\, T_\chi(x');$$

hence this defines a mapping S of A_N into A_χ and it can readily be verified that, *if A is without radical, S is an isomorphism of A_N onto A_χ.*

Property of the closure $\overline{P}_\chi$ of P_χ. We suppose A has no radical. From Proposition 5.2, Q_χ is the smallest ideal I satisfying $h(I) = \{\chi\}$; but saying that $h(I) = \{\chi\}$ amounts to saying that I is contained in a unique maximal ideal: N_χ; an ideal contained in a unique maximal ideal is said to be *primary*; now if we suppose A is *unitary* we get

$$Q_\chi = P_\chi \subset \overline{P}_\chi \subset N_\chi = T_\chi^{-1}(M_\chi) \subset A;$$

hence $\overline{P}_\chi$ is *the smallest closed primary ideal contained in N_χ.*

Examples

1. Take $A = \mathcal{D}^m_{[0,1]}$ (example (e)) and identify $\hat{A}$ with $[0, 1]$; for all $\chi \in [0, 1]$ the ideal $\overline{P}_\chi$ is the set of $x \in A$ satisfying

$$x(\chi) = x'(\chi) = \cdots = x^{(m)}(\chi) = 0$$

(see [18], § 11.9, where all the closed primary ideals of A are described); note that every closed ideal of A is the intersection of closed primary ideals (Šilov; see also [40]).

2. In Harmonic Analysis it is shown that in the algebra of example (f) any closed primary ideal is maximal.

Return to the proof of Corollary 5.1.

Suppose A is unitary; let I be a closed ideal of A; for all $\chi \in \hat{A}$ set $I_\chi = T_\chi(I)$; if $\chi \notin h(I)$, I_χ is equal to A_χ; on the other hand, by virtue of Theorem 5.1, we have

$$I = \bigcap_{\chi \in \hat{A}} T_\chi^{-1}(I_\chi)$$

hence

$$I = \bigcap_{\chi \in h(I)} T_\chi^{-1}(I_\chi);$$

we also have

$$k(h(I)) = \bigcap_{\chi \in h(I)} T_\chi^{-1}(M_\chi);$$

to show that $I = k(h(I))$ it will suffice thus to show that $I_\chi = M_\chi$ for all $\chi \in h(I)$; to do this we will introduce the following condition, which is less restrictive than (D)

(D′) for all $\chi \in \hat{A}$ we have $\overline{P}_\chi = N_\chi$.

Suppose first that $h(I)$ reduces to a point of χ; we have

$$P_\chi \subset I = T_\chi^{-1}(I_\chi) \subset N_\chi$$

whence, since I is closed, $I = N_\chi$ and $I_\chi = M_\chi$. Now if we only suppose $h(I)$ is discrete, every point χ of $h(I)$ admits an open neighbourhood U such that $U \cap h(I) = \{\chi\}$; U is the spectrum of $J = k(\hat{A} - U)$ and we can resume the preceding reasoning, replacing A by J.

Relation to the theory of sheaves

We no longer suppose A is regular; for each χ we denote by φ_χ the character of the algebra A_χ which associates to each germ its value at χ; let $\mathcal{A}$ be the sum set of the A_χ $(\chi \in \hat{A})$; each element x of A defines a mapping $\overline{x}$ of $\hat{A}$ into $\mathcal{A} : \overline{x}(\chi)$ is the germ of $\hat{x}$ at χ; if we endow $\mathcal{A}$ with the finest topology which makes the $\overline{x}$ continuous, $\mathcal{A}$ becomes a space spread in $\hat{A}$. Now if f belongs locally to $\mathcal{F}A$ at each point, we can define $\overline{f}$ in the same way; $\overline{f}$ is a continuous section of $\mathcal{A}$; conversely if s is a continuous section of $\mathcal{A}$, the function $f : \chi \to \varphi_\chi(s(\chi))$ belongs locally to $\mathcal{F}A$ at each point and we have $s = \overline{f}$; the algebra of the continuous sections of $\mathcal{A}$ is hence canonically isomorphic to the algebra of the functions belonging locally to $\mathcal{F}A$ at each point; hence to $\mathcal{F}A$ if A is regular, and to A if the latter is regular and has no radical.

The functions on $\hat{A}$ which are locally holomorphic functions of one or several functions $\hat{x}$ $(x \in A)$ (cf. § 2, ex. 2) are the sections of another sheaf, which is studied in [21], where a necessary and sufficient condition is given (in the form of the vanishing of a cohomology group) for any such function to belong to $\mathcal{F}A$.

CHAPTER VI

BANACH FUNCTION ALGEBRAS

In this chapter we will give a certain number of results without proof, referring for more details to a forthcoming Seminar; the reader in a hurry will find a more complete bibliography in [35].

§ 6.1. *Generalities*

Let X be a set; if complex functions on X form a Banach algebra A (for the usual operations and for a certain norm $\| \ \|$), these functions are bounded and the norm $\| \ \|$ is at least equal to the norm of uniform convergence: indeed, for all $x \in X$, $f \to f(x)$ is a morphism of A into $\mathfrak{C}$, hence of norm ≤ 1 (Corollary 1.8). Such an algebra has no radical and hence admits at most one Banach algebra topology (Corollary 2.1).

If the functions of A do not vanish simultaneously at any point of x (which will always be supposed in the sequel), we define a mapping T of X into $\hat{A}$ by associating with each x the character $f \to f(x)$; T is injective if and only if A is separating; if X is a topological space and if A is composed of continuous functions, T is continuous.

Case where the norm $\| \ \|$ *is equal to the norm of uniform convergence.*

The Gelfand transformation is isometric and its image $\mathcal{F}A$ is a closed subalgebra of $\mathscr{C}_0(\hat{A})$; suppose moreover that A contains the constants and is the closed subalgebra (resp. full closed) subalgebra generated by e and by a finite number of elements $f_1, \ldots, f_n$; we can identify $\hat{A}$ to a compact subset of $\mathfrak{C}^n$, namely $\mathrm{sp}(f_1, \ldots, f_n)$ (Proposition 2.9) which is polynomially convex (resp. rationally convex) (Proposition 2.10); finally it is clear that $\mathcal{F}A$ is identical to $\mathscr{P}(\hat{A})$ (resp. $\mathscr{R}(\hat{A})$).

Tensor products

Let X_1 and X_2 be two compact spaces, A_1 and A_2 Banach subalgebras of $\mathscr{C}(X_1)$ and $\mathscr{C}(X_2)$; the algebraic tensor product $A_1 \underset{\text{alg}}{\otimes} A_2$ can be considered as an algebra of functions on $X_1 \times X_2$, the function $(x_1, x_2) \to \sum f_{1,i}(x_1) \cdot f_{2,i}(x_2)$ corresponding to the element $\sum_{i=1}^{n} f_{1,i} \otimes f_{2,i}$ of $A_1 \underset{\text{alg}}{\otimes} A_2$; the completion of this algebra for the norm of uniform convergence (in general distinct from – – – and even non-equivalent to – – – that which was defined in § 2.6) will be denoted by $A_1 \otimes' A_2$.

For instance, it follows immediately from the Stone-Weierstrass theorem that $\mathscr{C}(X_1) \otimes' \mathscr{C}(X_2) = \mathscr{C}(X_1 \times X_2)$.

§ 6.2. *Separating closed subalgebras of $\mathscr{C}(X)$ (where X is a compact space) which contain the constants*

The mapping T is a homeomorphism of X onto *a* closed subset of $\hat{A}$, itself compact; if we identify X to this closed subset, the Gelfand transformation appears as an *extension* of the functions from A to $\hat{A}$; moreover bdry $A \subset X$.

The fundamental example for what follows is that of (d) considered as the algebra of functions on the circle $|z| = 1$; we will call it *example (d′)*.

no. 1. *Comparison of such an algebra A with $\mathscr{C}(X)$.*

– If A is self-adjoint (i.e. if $f \in A \Rightarrow \bar{f} \in A$), then $A = \mathscr{C}(X)$ (Stone-Weierstrass theorem for complex functions).

– If the real elements of A separate the points of X, then $A = \mathscr{C}(X)$ (Stone-Weierstrass theorem for real functions).

– If X is finite or countable, then $A = \mathscr{C}(X)$.

Indeed, let $f \in A$; its image $f(X)$ is finite or countable, hence (§ 6.3, no. 5) any function continuous on $f(X)$, and in particular the function $z \to \bar{z}$, is a uniform limit on $f(X)$ of restrictions of polynomials; then $\bar{f} \in A$ and A is self-adjoint.]

– If X is totally discontinuous and if $\hat{A} = X$, then $A = \mathscr{C}(X)$.

[Let x_1 and x_2 be two distinct elements of X; there exists an open and closed subset U of X containing x_1 and not x_2; the characteristic function of U belongs to A (Proposition 4.1), which proves that the real elements of A separate the points of X.]

– If the reals parts of the functions of A form a closed subspace of $\mathscr{C}(X, \mathfrak{R})$, then $A = \mathscr{C}(X)$.
([29])

– If X is the segment [0, 1] or the Cantor set, there exist non-trivial subalgebras A.
([39])

– It can happen that A is non-trivial even though $\hat{A} = \text{bdry } A = X$.

[Let X be the subset of $\mathfrak{R}^3$ defined by $x_1^2 + x_2^2 \leqq 1$ and $0 \leqq x_3 \leqq 1$ and A the subalgebra of $\mathscr{C}(X)$ composed of the functions whose restriction to the set Y ($x_3 = 0$) is holomorphic; we have $\hat{A} = X$ by virtue of the Propositions 2.5 and 2.6 applied to the ideal of the functions vanishing on Y; on the other hand bdry A contains $X - Y$ since any point of this set is a peak-point (cf. no. 2 below); hence bdry $A = X$.]

– It can happen that A is non-trivial and has the following property: if F_1 and F_2 are two closed disjoint subsets of X, there exists a function of A equal to 1 on F_1 and to 0 on F_2.
([31])

no. 2. *Peak-points*

A point x_0 of X is called a *peak-point* if there exists a function $f \in A$ such that $|f(x)| < |f(x_0)|$ for all $x \neq x_0$. Then x_0 admits a countable fundamental system of neighbourhoods: the sets defined by conditions $|f(x)| > |f(x_0)| - 1/n$.

Let P be the set of these points; we obviously have $P \subset \text{bdry } A$; in the case of example (d′) we have $P = X$.

Let χ_0 be a point of $\hat{A}$; suppose there exist a function f of A and a neighbourhood U of χ_0 such that $|\hat{f}(\chi)| < |\hat{f}(\chi_0)|$ for all $\chi \in U - \{\chi_0\}$; then $\chi_0 \in P$ ("Local maximum principle", [34]).

Case of metrizable X. Each function $|f|$ ($f \in A$) reaches its maximum on P ([23]); since on the other hand any set with this property obviously contains P, P is the smallest set which has this property; whence the name "minimal boundary" which is sometimes given to it; moreover $\overline{P} = \text{bdry } A$. Further P is a G_δ ([23]); considered as a set of continuous linear forms, P is the set of extreme points of the compact convex set composed of the continuous linear forms φ satisfying $\|\varphi\| \leqq 1$ and $\varphi(e) = 1$ ([24]).

no. 3. *Integral representation of the characters.*

For all $\chi \in \hat{A}$ there exists a positive measure with norm 1 (in general it is not unique), μ_χ, on X such that $\chi(f) = \mu_\chi(f)$ for all $f \in A$. [Indeed, χ is a continuous linear form with norm 1 on A and, by virtue of the Hahn-Banach theorem, extends into a continuous linear form of norm 1 on $\mathscr{C}(X)$; i.e. a measure μ_χ with norm 1 on X; μ_χ is positive because $\mu_\chi(e) = 1$; this reasoning even shows that we can take μ_χ concentrated on bdry A.]

This result generalizes the Cauchy integral formula, example (d′) (cf. no. 4 below). If X is metrizable, we can take μ_χ concentrated on P ([24]).

no. 4. *Dirichlet algebras.*

A subalgebra A is called a *Dirichlet* algebra if the real parts of its elements are everywhere dense in $\mathscr{C}(X, \mathfrak{R})$.

This is the case in example (d′).

[Indeed, we have, among others, as the real parts of elements of A the functions $\theta \to \cos n\theta$ and $\theta \to \sin n\theta$.]

The name is due to the fact that the following problem (abstract Dirichlet problem) is solvable: given a real continuous function on X, approximate it uniformly by restrictions of real parts of functions $\hat{f}$ where $f \in A$. For all $\chi \in \hat{A}$ the measure μ_χ is then unique; for the example (d′) and the character corresponding to a point $re^{i\varphi}$, $r < 1$, μ_χ is the measure on X defined by the density $\theta \to {}^1/_{(2\pi)} \cdot (1 - r^2)/(1 + r^2 - 2r\cos(\theta - \varphi))$ (Poisson kernel). The uniqueness of μ_χ implies that bdry $A = X$ [take $\chi \in X$ and μ_χ concentrated on bdry A]; for the same reason, if X is metrizable, $P = X$.

The forthcoming study of Dirichlet algebras concerns principally the spaces $H^p(\mu_\chi)$ or closed subspaces of the $L^p(X, \mu_\chi)$ generated by A; one generalize for them some classical results concerning example (d′); see also [39], § 4.

no. 5. *Real elements of A.*

We have already said that if they separate the points of X we get $A = \mathscr{C}(X)$; the opposite case is that where the only real elements of A are the constants; this is so, in particular, in example (d′). In the general case one generalize the Stone-Weierstrass theorem in the following manner: write $x_1 \sim x_2$ if $f(x_1) = f(x_2)$ for every real function $f \in A$; then if a continuous function g on X coincides on every class with respect to $\sim$ with an element of A, we have $g \in A$ (see [11], § 44).

no. 6. *Subalgebras A which are maximal among the subalgebras of $\mathscr{C}(X)$.*

This is the case in example (d′) ([39], § 3); the general case involves some results which are classical in this particular case; if A contains no non-constant real function, every function of A which vanishes on a non-empty open set of X vanishes; if $\chi \in \hat{A} - X$ and if $f \in A$ is not constant, then $|\hat{f}(\chi)| < \|f\|$ ([39], § 3).

no. 7. In [39], § 10 and in [26], § 8 one will find results concerning the possibility of endowing $\hat{A}$ with a structure of complex analytic manifold for which the functions $\hat{f}$ are analytic.

Later we will consider self-adjoint closed subalgebras of $\mathscr{C}^\infty(X)$ (where X is a topological space): § 7.4, ex. 5 and § 8.1.

§ 6.3. *Banach algebras of holomorphic functions*

(For futher details, see Topological algebras and holomorphic functions.)

We will merely consider algebras of functions holomorphic on subsets of spaces $\mathfrak{C}^n$; but some results remain valid if we replace $\mathfrak{C}^n$ by an analytic manifold or even by a complex analytic space (cf. [26]).

no. 1. *Definition.*

Given a compact subset X of $\mathfrak{C}^n$, we can consider the following Banach algebras:

– $\mathscr{P}(X)$ = closure in $\mathscr{C}(X)$ of the set of restrictions of polynomials

– $\mathscr{R}(X)$ = closure in $\mathscr{C}(X)$ of the set of restrictions of rational fractions regular on X

– $\mathscr{H}_1(X)$ = closure in $\mathscr{C}(X)$ of the set of restrictions of functions holomorphic in the neighbourhood of X

– $\mathscr{S}(X)$ = subalgebra of $\mathscr{C}(X)$ composed of the functions holomorphic on the interior of X.

We have the following inclusions:

$$\mathscr{P}(X) \subset \mathscr{R}(X) \subset \mathscr{H}_1(X) \subset \mathscr{S}(X) \subset \mathscr{C}(X);$$

$\mathscr{S}(X) = \mathscr{C}(X)$ if and only if X has no interior; all that was said in the beginning of § 6.2 is valid for all these algebras.

no. 2. *Spectra.*

– The spectrum of $\mathscr{P}(X)$ is identified with the polynomially convex hull Y of X (cf. Appendix I), the character of $\mathscr{P}(X)$ defined by $\chi(P) = P(z_0)$ for any polynomial P corresponding to any point z_0 of Y.

[Indeed, the mapping $\mathscr{P} \mid Y \to P \mid X$ is isometric, hence extends into an isomorphism of $\mathscr{P}(Y)$ onto $\mathscr{P}(X)$; the assertion follows hence from Proposition 2.11.]

– The spectrum of $\mathscr{R}(X)$ is identified analoguosly and for the same reason with the rationally convex hull of X.

– The spectrum of $\mathscr{H}_1(X)$ is related to what L. Waelbroeck calls "holomorphy closure" of X (cf. part III of this book, th. 2.8); one proves, using non-normed algebras, that $\mathscr{H}_1(X)$ has spectrum X if X is the intersection of a sequence of neighbourhoods which are domains of holomorphy; see also [26], Theorem 10.7.

– Finding the spectrum of $\mathscr{S}(X)$ seems a lot more difficult.

no. 3. *Boundaries.*

We obviously have

bdry $\mathscr{P}(X) \subset$ bdry $\mathscr{R}(X) \subset$ bdry $\mathscr{H}_1(X) \subset$ bdry $\mathscr{S}(X) \subset$ top. bdry. of X.

If $n = 1$ we have bdry $\mathscr{R}(X) =$ top. bdry. of X, from Proposition 2.3; hence

bdry $\mathscr{R}(X) =$ bdry $\mathscr{H}_1(X) =$ bdry $\mathscr{S}(X) =$ top. bdry. of X. However for $n > 1$ we can have bdry $\mathscr{H}_1(X) \neq$ top. bdry. of X.

[Indeed, take $X \subset \mathfrak{C}^2$ defined by $|z_1| \leqq 1$ and $|z_2| \leqq 1$; the topological boundary of X is the set defined by $|z_1| = 1$ or $|z_2| = 1$ and bdry $\mathscr{H}_1(X)$ is the set defined by $|z_1| = |z_2| = 1$ as can be seen from a reasoning analogous to that of Proposition 2.3]

We can also have bdry $\mathscr{S}(X) \neq$ top. bdry. of X ([22]). In [34′] one will find a study of the peak-points of some of these algebras.

no. 4. *General properties.*

– If X is polynomially convex, we have $\mathscr{P}(X) = \mathscr{H}_1(X)$ (see the proof of Theorem 4.2).

– If X is rationally convex, we have $\mathscr{R}(X) = \mathscr{H}_1(X)$ (analogous proof).

– If X is the closure of a convex open set U, we have $\mathscr{H}_1(X) = \mathscr{S}(X)$.

[Let $z_0 \in U$ and let $f \in \mathscr{S}(X)$; f is holomorphic on U, hence the function $f_\varepsilon : z \to f(\varepsilon z_0 + (1 - \varepsilon)z)$ is holomorphic in the neighbourhood of X; then f is the uniform limit of the f_ε; note that this argument has already been carried out in § 1.5, example (d); it can naturally be extended to more general sets.]

– Let (for $i = 1, 2$) X_i be a compact subset of $\mathfrak{C}^{n_i}$ such that $\mathscr{H}_1(X_i)$ has spectrum X_i; then

$$\mathscr{H}_1(X_1) \otimes' \mathscr{H}_1(X_2) = \mathscr{H}_1(X_1 \times X_2).$$

[We trivially find the inclusion $\subset$; it is then easy to see that the first member has spectrum $X_1 \times X_2$ and the reasoning is continued as for theorem 4.2.]

no. 5. *The case* $n = 1$.

– Any compact subset of $\mathfrak{C}$ being rationally convex (cf. Appendix I) we always have $\mathscr{R}(X) = \mathscr{H}_1(X)$ and hence $\widehat{\mathscr{R}(X)} = \widehat{\mathscr{H}_1(X)} = X$.

– (Recall that in Corollary 2.3 we gave a characterization of the polynomially convex compact subsets of $\mathfrak{C}$.)

If X is polynomially convexe we have $\mathscr{P}(X) = \mathscr{S}(X)$ ([33]) and hence

$$\mathscr{P}(X) = \mathscr{R}(X) = \mathscr{H}_1(X) = \mathscr{S}(X)$$

$$\widehat{\mathscr{P}(X)} = \widehat{\mathscr{R}(X)} = \widehat{\mathscr{H}_1(X)} = \widehat{\mathscr{S}(X)} = X;$$

if moreover X has no interior, these algebras are also equal to $\mathscr{C}(X)$; this result remains valid if $n > 1$ and if X is an analytic arc ([39′]).

– We can have $\mathscr{H}_1(X) \neq \mathscr{S}(X)$ even though X is always rationally convex.

[Let D be the open disc $|z| < 1$ and $D_1, D_2, \ldots$ open discs contained in D and such that

(i) the D_i are disjoint two by two

(ii) $X = \overline{D} - \bigcup D_i$ has no interior

(iii) the sum of the lengths of the circumferences C_i bounding the D_i is finite; define a measure μ on X by taking the Lebesgue measures in the positive sense on $|z| = 1$ and in the negative sense on each of the C_i; μ is zero on any function holomorphic in the neighbourhood of X, hence on $\mathscr{H}_1(X)$, whence $\mathscr{H}_1(X) \neq \mathscr{C}(X) = \mathscr{S}(X)$. This example is known as the "Swiss cheese" set.]

– We have $\mathscr{R}(X) = \mathscr{C}(X)$ if X has no interior and if $\mathfrak{C} - X$ has only a finite number of connected components; or else if X has zero measure for the Lebesgue measure ([33]).

– In [16], Chapter 6, one will find a detailed study of $\mathscr{S}(X)$ in the case of the closed disc $|z| \leqq 1$, in particular the description of its closed ideals.

no. 6. There exist other Banach algebras of holomorphic functions, for instance, for any open subset $U \subset \mathfrak{C}^n$, the algebra $H^\infty(U)$ of the bounded holomorphic functions on U; in [16], Chapter 10, one will find results concerning the case of the open disc D: $|z| < 1$ (spectrum, Šilov boundary); it has recently been found that D is everywhere dense in the spectrum of this algebra (L. Carleson, Stockholm Congress, 1962).

But there also exist very important algebras of holomorphic functions which are not Banach algebras, for instance the algebra $\mathscr{O}(U)$ of all functions holomorphic on an open subset U of $\mathfrak{C}^n$.

Certain non-Banach algebras are however sufficiently close to being Banach algebras for the present theory to be applicable to them; as an example, denote by X a polynomially convex compact subset of $\mathfrak{C}^n$ (it suffices in fact to suppose that $\mathscr{H}_1(X)$ has spectrum X) and by $f_1, \ldots, f_p$ elements of $\mathscr{O}(X)$ having no common zero in X, and show that there exist elements $g_1, \ldots, g_p$ of $\mathscr{O}(X)$ satisfying $\sum f_i g_i = 1$ in the sense of $\mathscr{O}(X)$ *(Cartan's theorem of the zeros)*; by the hypothesis made on $\mathscr{H}_1(X)$ there exist elements $h_1, \ldots, h_p$ of $\mathscr{H}_1(X)$ satisfying $\sum f_i g_i = 1$ on X, then functions $h_1', \ldots, h_p'$ holomorphic in the neighbourhood of X such that $\| \sum f_i h_i' - 1 \| \leqq \frac{1}{2}$ in the sense of $\mathscr{H}_1(X)$; then $K = \sum f_i h_i'$ admits an inverse $1/k$ holomorphic in the neighbourhood of X and it suffices to set $g_i = h_i'/k$.

CHAPTER VII

COMMUTATIVE BANACH ALGEBRAS WITH INVOLUTION

We call a *commutative Banach algebra with involution* (or more briefly C. B. A. I.) any commutative Banach algebra which is also endowed with an involution (cf. § 0.6) satisfying $\|x^*\| = \|x\|$.

Examples. The algebras of examples (a), (b), (c), (e), (f), (g), where the involution is the passage to the conjugate complex function; (d), setting $f^*(z) = \overline{f(\bar{z})}$; (h), taking as H a Hilbert space, as A a self-adjoint commutative closed subalgebra of $\mathscr{L}(H)$ and as involution the passage to the adjoint operator.

§ 7.1. *Positive linear forms*

Proposition 7.1. Every positive linear form f is continuous on a unitary C. B. A. I. and has norm $f(e)$.

We first take x hermitian with norm $\leqq 1$; the element

$$y = e + \sum_{n=1}^{\infty} \tfrac{1}{2} \cdot (\tfrac{1}{2} - 1) \ldots (\tfrac{1}{2} - n + 1)\, x^n/n!$$

is hermitian and its square is $e - x$; hence $f(e - x) \geqq 0$ i.e. $f(x) \leqq f(e)$; similarly $f(-x) \leqq f(e)$, whence $|f(x)| \leqq f(e)$. Then if x is an arbitrary hermitian element we will have $|f(x) \leqq f(e) \cdot \|x\|$. Finally if x is an arbitrary element of A

$$|f(x)|^2 \leqq f(e) \cdot f(xx^*) \leqq (f(e))^2 \cdot \|xx^*\| \leqq (f(e))^2 \cdot \|x\|^2$$

which proves that f is continuous and has norm $\leqq f(e)$; $\|f\| = f(e)$ is obtained by taking $x = e$.

Corollary 7.1. Every positive extendable form is continuous on an arbitrary C. B. A. I.

Proposition 7.2. On a unitary C. B. A. I., every positive form f satisfies

$$|f(x)| \leqq f(e) \cdot \nu(x)$$

and, in particular, vanishes on the radical.

Indeed, from Schwarz's inequality

$$f(xx^*) \leqq f(e)^{\frac{1}{2}} \cdot (f((xx^*)^2))^{\frac{1}{2}}$$

$$\leqq f(e)^{\frac{1}{2}+\frac{1}{4}} \cdot (f((xx^*)^4))^{\frac{1}{4}}$$

$$\cdot \quad \cdot \quad \cdot \quad \cdot \quad \cdot \quad \cdot \quad \cdot \quad \cdot$$

$$\leqq f(e)^{\frac{1}{2}+\cdots\frac{1}{2^n}} \cdot (f((xx^*)^{2^n}))^{\frac{1}{2^n}}$$

$$\leqq f(e)^{\frac{1}{2}+\cdots\frac{1}{2^n}} \cdot f(e)^{\frac{1}{2^n}} \cdot \|(xx^*)^{2^n}\|^{\frac{1}{2^n}}$$

whence, in the limit,

$$f(xx^*) \leqq f(e) \cdot \nu(xx^*)$$

and finally

$$|f(x)| \leqq f(e)^{\frac{1}{2}} \cdot (f(xx^*))^{\frac{1}{2}} \leqq f(e) \cdot (\nu(xx^*))^{\frac{1}{2}} \leqq f(e) \cdot \nu(x).$$

Corollary 7.2. On an arbitrary C. B. A. I. every positive extendable form f satisfies

$$|f(x)| \leqq k \cdot \nu(x)$$

and, in particular, vanishes on the radical.

Proposition 7.3. On a C. B. A. I. admitting an approximate unit (e_i), any positive form f is hermitian, continuous, extendable and has norm $\lim_i f(e_i e_i^*)$.

We first prove that f is continuous; it suffices to prove that

$$x_n \to 0 \Rightarrow f(x_n) \to 0$$

or again (Proposition 1.4) that

$$x_n \to 0 \Rightarrow f(yzx_n) \to 0 \qquad \forall y \text{ and } z \in A$$

or finally, by virtue of the identity

$$4yz = (y + z^*)(y + z^*)^* - (y - z^*)(y - z^*)^* + i(y + iz^*)(y + iz^*)^*$$
$$- i(y - iz^*)(y - iz^*)^* \qquad (1)$$

that

$$x_n \to 0 \Rightarrow f(yy^*x_n) \to 0 \quad \forall y \in A;$$

now we define a positive form on A by setting $g(x) = f(yy^*x)$ and the assertion follows from Proposition 7.1; we note in passing the following inequality

$$|f(yy^*x)| \leqq f(yy^*) \cdot \|x\|. \tag{2}$$

Then f is hermitian since (§ 0.7) $f(e_i^*x^*) = \overline{f(e_ix)}$ whence, at the limit, $f(x^*) = f(x)$. Then f is extendable because

$$|f(e_ix)|^2 \leqq f(e_ie_i^*) \cdot f(xx^*) \leqq \|f\| \cdot f(xx^*)$$

whence, at the limit,

$$|f(x)|^2 \leqq \|f\| \cdot f(xx^*). \tag{3}$$

Finally let $\varepsilon > 0$ and let x be such that $\|x\| = 1$ and $|f(x)| \geqq \|f\| - \varepsilon$; $e_ie_i^*x$ tends to x (it suffices to write x in the form x_1x_2); there exists hence an i_0 such that $i \geqq i_0$ implies $|f(e_ie_i^*x)| \geqq |f(x)| - \varepsilon$; then

$$\|f\| \geqq f(e_ie_i^*) \geqq |f(e_ie_i^*x)| \geqq |f(x)| - \varepsilon \geqq \|f\| - 2\varepsilon$$

which shows that indeed $f(e_ie_i^*) \to \|f\|$.

Remark 7.1. With the previous hypotheses we have $|f(x)| \leqq \|f\| \cdot \nu(x)$ because, from (3), the number k in Corollary 7.2 and § 0.7 can be taken to be equal to $\|f\|$.

Exercise. The hypotheses and the notations being those of Proposition 7.3, show that $\|f\| = \lim f(e_i)$.

[Consider the prehilbert structure on A defined by the scalar product $(x \mid x') = f(xx'^*)$; show that for this structure $e_ie_i^* \to e$; then that $e_j \to e$ by writing

$$e_j - e = (e_j - e_je_ie_i^*) + (e_je_ie_i^* - e_ie_i^*) + (e_ie_i^* - e)\,]$$

§ 7.2. *Hermitian characters*

The mapping $\chi \to \chi^*$ (see § 0.6) is a homeomorphism of $\hat{A}$ onto itself, such that the fixed points are the hermitian characters; these form thus a closed subset of $\hat{A}$, which we will denote by $\hat{A}^h$; they are continuous positive forms.

Examples. It is clear that for the examples (b), (c), (e), (f) all the characters are hermitian; we will see in the following section that this is also for the examples (a), (g) and (h); for example (d) the hermitian characters are those which correspond to the points of the real segment $[-1, +1]$; finally we give an example of an algebra without any hermitian characters: let $X \subset \mathfrak{C}$ be the union of the two discs

$$|z - 2i| \leqq 1 \quad \text{and} \quad |z + 2i| \leqq 1$$

and let $A = \mathscr{P}(X)$; let us define the involution by $f^*(z) = \overline{f(\bar{z})}$; the characters of A correspond bijectively to the points of X (cf. for instance § 6.3, no. 2) and it is clear that none of them is hermitian.

For all $x \in A$ we denote by $\hat{x}^h$ the restriction of $\hat{x}$ to $\hat{A}^h$; the mapping $x \to \hat{x}^h$ of A into $\mathscr{C}_0(\hat{A}^h)$ is a *morphism of *-algebras*, whereas $x \to \hat{x}$ is not in general such a morphism.

Proposition 7.4. The functions $\hat{x}^h$ $(x \in A)$ form an everywhere dense self-adjoint subalgebra of $\mathscr{C}_0(\hat{A}^h)$.

This algebra is obviously self-adjoint, hence everywhere dense by virtue of the Stone-Weierstrass theorem.

Properties of algebras all of whose characters are hermitian.

They are sometimes called "symmetric" or "completely symmetric" or "A^*-algebras". Let A be such an algebra; the spectrum of any hermitian element is real; $\mathscr{F}A$ is an everywhere dense self-adjoint subalgebra of $\mathscr{C}_0(\hat{A})$, whence we deduce that bdry $A = \hat{A}$; if A is a subalgebra of a C. B. A. B (where A and B have the same unit element) any character of A extends into a character of B and $\hat{A}$ is a quotient of $\hat{B}$ (cf. Proposition 2.4 and Corollary 2.2); hence $\operatorname{sp}_A x = \operatorname{sp}_B x$ for all $x \in A$; in particular A is a full subalgebra of B. Finally if A is generated by an element x, the mapping $\chi \to \chi(x)$ of $\hat{A}$ onto sp x is a homeomorphism.

Exercise. All the characters of a unitary C. B. A. I. A are hermitian if and only if all the elements $e + xx^*$ are invertible.

§ 7.3. C^*-*algebras*

Definition. A commutative Banach algebra with involution is called an C^*-*algebra* if $\|xx^*\| = \|x\|^2$ for all x; it is also called a "completely regular" algebra or "B^*-algebra".

Examples. The algebras of examples (a), (b), (c), (g), (h).

Lemma 7.1. For any commutative C^*-algebra the Gelfand transformation is isometric.

First, for all hermitian x,

$$\|x\| = \|x^2\|^{\frac{1}{2}} = \|x^4\|^{\frac{1}{4}} = \cdots = \|x^{2^n}\|^{\frac{1}{2^n}}$$

hence $\|x\| = \nu(x)$; then, for arbitrary x,

$$\|x\|^2 = \|xx^*\| = \nu(xx^*) \leqq \nu(x) \cdot \nu(x^*) = (\nu(x))^2.$$

Lemma 7.2. Every character of a commutative C^*-algebra is hermitian.

We first prove that any character in bdry A is hermitian; suppose this is not true: $\chi_0 \in$ bdry A and $\chi_0 \neq \chi_0^*$; there exists an open neighbourhood U of χ_0 which is disjoint from its transform U^*; then there exists an $x \in A$ such that

$$u = \sup_{\chi \in \hat{A} - U} |\hat{x}(\chi)| < \sup_{\chi \in U} |\hat{x}(\chi)| = v;$$

then

$$u = \sup_{\chi \in \hat{A} - U^*} |\widehat{x^*}(\chi)| < \sup_{\chi \in U^*} |\widehat{x^*}(\chi)| = v;$$

for all χ we have $\chi \in \hat{A} - U$ or $\chi \in \hat{A} - U^*$, hence

$$|\widehat{xx^*}(\chi)| \leqq uv$$

$$\|xx^*\| = \sup_{\chi \in \hat{A}} |\widehat{xx^*}(\chi)| \leqq uv < v^2 = \|x\|^2$$

whence a contradiction.

This being so, the mapping $x \to \hat{x} \mid \text{bdry } A$ of A into $\mathscr{C}_0(\text{bdry } A)$ is a $*$-algebra morphism; its image is everywhere dense in $\mathscr{C}_0(\text{bdry } A)$ and since it is isometric, it is an isomorphism of A onto $\mathscr{C}_0(\text{bdry } A)$; but we know that the characters of the latter algebra are all hermitian. In short

Theorem 7.1. (Gelfand-Naïmark). The Gelfand transformation is an isometric isomorphism of A onto $\mathscr{C}_0(\hat{A})$ for any commutative C^*-algebra A.

Corollary 7.3. Every closed ideal of A is self-adjoint and an intersection of regular maximal ideals.

Moreover all that was said at the end of § 7.2 can be applied to these algebras.

Corollary 7.4. Every morphism of a C. B. A. into a commutative C^*-algebra decreases the norms.

Corollary 7.5. There is at most one norm on a commutative $*$-algebra A for which A is a C^*-algebra.

(This completes the Corollary 2.1.)

Remark 7.2. Theorem 7.1 allows us to improve considerably the functional calculus described in Chapter IV; indeed, let $f \in \mathscr{C}(\mathrm{sp}(a_1, \ldots, a_n))$; there exists a unique element b such that

$$\hat{b}(\chi) = f(\hat{a}_1(\chi), \ldots, \hat{a}_n(\chi)) \qquad \forall \chi \in \hat{A};$$

setting $b = f(a_1, \ldots, a_n)$ we see that the mapping $f \to f(a_1, \ldots, a_n)$ is an isometric morphism of $\mathscr{C}(\mathrm{sp}(a_1, \ldots, a_n))$ into A and that $f(a_1, \ldots, a_n)$ has the same meaning as in Chapter IV if f is holomorphic in the neighbourhood of $\mathrm{sp}(a_1, \ldots, a_n)$. This will be improved further for a particular case, in § 8.2.

Exercises. (We recommend that they be done in the order indicated).

1. If A is a non-unitary commutative C^*-algebra, there exists on $\tilde{A}$ a norm for which it is a C^*-algebra: $\|x + \lambda e\|$ is the norm of the operator $y \to xy + \lambda y$ in A; in general it is distinct from the norm defined in § 1.1.
   [Can be proved directly or by using Theorem 7.1.]
2. The quotient of a commutative C^*-algebra by a closed ideal is a C^*-algebra; cf. § 2.6, example following Proposition 2.6.
3. Every injective morphism of a commutative C^*-algebra into another is isometric.

[Let $T: A \to B$; we can suppose A and B are unitary, where T transforms unit into unit; show, by contradiction, that the mapping $\chi \to \chi \circ T$ of $\hat{B}$ into $\hat{A}$ is surjective].

4. If T is a morphism of a commutative C^*-algebra A into a commutative C^*-algebra B, $T(A)$ is closed in B.
5. Describe the closed self-adjoint subalgebras of $\mathscr{C}_0(X)$ (where X is a locally compact space).

§ 7.4. *Integral representations of positive linear forms*

In all this section A denotes a *C. B. A. I. which admits an approximate unit* (e_i); we will see that the positive forms on A are identified with the positive forms on a certain commutative C^*-algebra, and that they are closely related to the set $\hat{A}^h$ of hermitian characters of A.

Denote by I the set of $x \in A$ satisfying $f(xx^*) = 0$ for any positive form f; this is equivalent, from the Schwarz inequality, to $f(xy) = 0$ for all f and all $y \in A$ and implies that $f(x) = 0$ since such an f is continuous; we see that I is a closed self-adjoint ideal of A. There is a bijective correspondence between the positive forms on A and the positive forms on A/I:

$$f \leftrightarrow \dot{f} \qquad \text{with} \qquad \dot{f}(\dot{x}) = f(x); \tag{4}$$

consequently for any non-zero element y of A/I there exists a positive form g on A/I such that $g(yy^*) > 0$; set

$$p(y) = (\sup g(yy^*))^{\frac{1}{2}}$$

where the upper bound is taken for all the positive forms g on A/I with norm $\leqq 1$; to establish that p is an involutive algebra norm, the only tricky point is the inequality

$$p(y_1y_2) \leqq p(y_1) \cdot p(y_2); \qquad \text{but} \qquad g(y_1y_1^*) = 0 \Rightarrow g(y_1y_1^*y_2y_2^*) = 0$$

hence

$$p(y_1y_2) = (\sup g(y_1y_1^*y_2y_2^*))^{\frac{1}{2}}$$

where the upper bound is taken for the g with norm $\leqq 1$ which satisfy $g(y_1y_1^*) > 0$; for such a g the function

$$y_2 \to g'(y_2) = g(y_1y_1^*y_2) \,/\, g(y_1y_1^*)$$

is a positive form on A/I with norm $\leqq 1$, from (2), and we have

$$p(y_1y_2) = (\sup g(y_1y_1^*) \cdot g'(y_2y_2^*))^{\frac{1}{2}} \leqq p(y_1) \cdot p(y_2).$$

The norm p satisfies

$$p(yy^*) = (p(y))^2;$$

indeed, $p(yy^*) \geqq (p(y))^2$ follows from (3) where we replace f by g and x by yy^* and on the other hand $p(yy^*) \leqq (p(y))^2$ is obvious; the completion of A/I for the norm p is hence a *commutative C^*-algebra* which we will denote by A' (A' is sometimes called the "enveloping" C^*-algebra of A and A/I "reduced algebra" of A).

Let g be a positive form on A/I; for all $y \in A/I$ with $p(y) \leqq 1$ we have

$$|g(y)|^2 \leqq \|g\|_{A/I} \cdot g(yy^*) \quad \text{from (3)}$$
$$\leqq \|g\|^2_{A/I} \quad \text{from the definition of } p;$$

this proves that g is continuous for the norm p and that $\|g\|_p \leqq \|g\|_{A/I}$; but since the norm p, for the elements of A/I, is smaller than the first norm, we also have $\|g\|_p \leqq \|g\|_{A/I}$; hence

$$\|g\|_p = \|g\|_{A/I} \quad \text{for every positive form } g$$

and there is an isometric bijective correspondence between positive forms on A/I and positive forms on A'; taking (4) into account we see that there is an *isometric bijective correspondence between positive forms on A and positive forms on A'*.

Then, on A as well as on A', the multiplicative positive forms are exactly the hermitian characters; since all the characters of A' are hermitian we see, in particular, that there'is a bijective correspondence between hermitian characters of A and characters of A'; and finally a homeomorphism between $\hat{A}^h$ and $\hat{A}'$. Finally, since the intersection of the kernels of the characters of A' is empty, the intersection of the kernels of the hermitian characters of A is equal to I.

In short, we can state the following results:

Proposition 7.5. Let I be the closed self-adjoint ideal of A composed of the x such that $f(xx^*) = 0$ for any positive form f; the completion of A/I for the norm

$p(y) = (\sup g(yy^*))^{\frac{1}{2}}$, where g is a positive form with norm $\leqq 1$ on A/I

is a C^*-algebra whose positive forms are in bijective and isometric correspondence with those of A, and the characters – – – with the hermitian characters of A.

Remark 7.3. If an element of A is annuled by all the hermitian characters, it is annuled by all the positive forms.

Theorem 7.2. (Bochner-Raïkov). The formula $f(x) = \mu(\hat{x}^h)$ establishes a bijective and isometric correspondence between positive forms on A and positive bounded measures on $\hat{A}^h$.

Corollary 7.6. The hermitian characters of A and the zero form are exactly the extreme points of the set of positive forms with norm $\leqq 1$.

Corollary 7.7. Any positive form on A is the weak limit of linear combinations with positives coefficients of hermitian characters.

This follows from the preceding corollary and the Krein-Milman theorem.

Remark 7.4. We denote by P the set of positive forms with norm $\leqq 1$; the formula of Theorem 7.2 can be written

$$f(x) = \int_{\hat{A}^h} \hat{x}(\chi) \cdot \mathrm{d}\mu(\chi) = \int_{\hat{A}^h} \chi(x) \cdot \mathrm{d}\mu(\chi)$$

or

$$f = \int_{\hat{A}^h} \chi \cdot \mathrm{d}\mu(\chi);$$

when it is in this form one sees more readily that it permits the decomposition of any positive form into an integral of hermitian characters; in other words, the representation of any point of P as the barycentre of a measure concentrated on the set of extreme points of P.

Remarks 7.5. In the beginning of § 7.2 we gave an example of a C. B. A. I. having no hermitian characters; we see now that this algebra also admits no non-zero positive forms.

In the following proposition we suppose, to simplify notations, that A has only hermitian characters; in fact everything remains valid without this hypothesis on condition that $\hat{A}$ be replaced by $\hat{A}^h$.

Proposition 7.6. Let A be a C. B. A. I. all of whose characters are hermitian, and admitting an approximate unit; let I be an everywhere dense self-adjoint ideal of A and φ a positive form on I; there exists a positive measure μ on $\hat{A}$ such that, if $z \in I^2$, $\hat{z}$ is μ-integrable and $\varphi(xz) = \mu(\hat{x}\hat{z})$ for all $x \in A$.

Denote by E the set of elements of the form $\sum_{j=1}^{n} z_j z_j^* \ (z_j \in I)$; for all $z \in E$ the mapping $\varphi_z : x \to \varphi(zx)$ is a positive form on A, hence of form

$$\varphi(zx) = \mu_z(\hat{x}),$$

where μ_z is a bounded positive measure on $\hat{A}$; note that if z' is another element of E we have

$$\mu_z(\hat{x}\hat{z}') = \mu_{z'}(\hat{x}\hat{z}) \qquad \forall x \in A$$

and, by continuity,

$$\mu_z(f\hat{z}') = \mu_{z'}(f\hat{z}) \qquad \forall f \in \mathscr{C}_0(\hat{A}).$$

Let $g \in \mathscr{K}(\hat{A})$ --- the set of continuous functions with compact support on $\hat{A}$; for all $\chi \in$ support g there is a $y_\chi \in I$ such that $\hat{y}_\chi(\chi) \neq 0$; by a compacity argument we deduce an element z such that

$$z \in E \quad \text{and} \quad \hat{z} > 0 \quad \text{on the support of } g; \tag{5}$$

define $g/\hat{z} \in \mathscr{K}(\hat{A})$, with the convention that $0/0 = 0$; show that the number $\mu_z(g/\hat{z})$ is independent of the choice of z satisfying (5); if z' is another such element we have indeed

$$\mu_z(g/\hat{z}) = \mu_z(g/\hat{z}\hat{z}' \cdot \hat{z}') = \mu_{z'}(g/\hat{z}\hat{z}' \cdot \hat{z}) = \mu_{z'}(g/\hat{z}');$$

this being so, we can set

$$\mu(g) = \mu_z(g/\hat{z}); \qquad \text{where } z \text{ is an arbitrary element satisfying (5);}$$

we see immediately that we are defining a positive measure μ on A.

We now take $g \in \mathscr{K}(A)$, $y \in E$ and z satisfying (5); we get

$$\mu(g\hat{y}) = \mu_z(g/\hat{z} \cdot \hat{y}) = \mu_y(g/\hat{z} \cdot \hat{z}) = \mu_y(g);$$

in other words, μ_y is equal to the product of μ by $\hat{y}$; since μ_y is bounded, $\hat{y}$ is μ-integrable ([8], § 5, Theorem 1 and Corollary, and § 2, Proposition 2); if $x \in A$ we get

$$\varphi(xy) = \varphi_y(x) = \mu_y(\hat{x}) = \mu(\hat{x}\hat{y});$$

finally if $z \in I^2$, by virtue of the identity (1) z is a linear combination of elements of E, $\hat{z}$ is μ-integrable and we also get

$$\varphi(xz) = \mu(\hat{x}\hat{z}).$$

Remark 7.6. The reasoning above shows in fact that $\hat{y}$ is μ-integrable and that $\varphi(xy) = \mu(\hat{x}\hat{y})$ for all $y \in I$ such that the linear form on $A : x \to \varphi(xy)$ is positive. If A is unitary we also have $\varphi(y) = \mu(\hat{y})$.

CHAPTER VIII

MISCELLANEOUS APPLICATIONS

§ 8.1. *Compactifications*

Let X be a topological space and A a subalgebra of $\mathscr{C}^\infty(X)$ with the following properties:

(i) A is closed

(ii) A is self-adjoint (i.e. $f \in A \Rightarrow \bar{f} \in A$)

(iii) A contains the constant functions

(iv) for every closed subset F of X and every $x \in X - F$ there exists an $f \in A$ which vanishes on F and is non-vanishing at x.

It is clear that if such an algebra exists, X is *completely regular*.

Using the notations of § 6.1, we set $Y = \hat{A}$; T is an injective and continuous mapping of X into Y; since A is a C^*-algebra, the Gelfand transformation is an isometric isomorphism of A onto $\mathscr{C}(Y)$; the inverse transformation is the mapping $g \to g \circ T$; $T(X)$ is everywhere dense in Y because otherwise there would exist a non-zero element of $\mathscr{C}(Y)$ which vanishes on $T(X)$ and it could not be of the form $\hat{f}$ ($f \in A$); finally T is a homeomorphism of X onto $T(X)$; to see this take F closed in X and show that $T(F) = \overline{T(F)} \cap T(X)$; let $y = T(x) \in T(X) - T(F)$, $x \in X - F$; there exists an $f \in A$ zero on F and non-zero at x; then $\hat{f}$ is zero on $T(F)$, non-zero at y, hence $y \notin \overline{T(F)}$.

We have thus constructed a couple (Y, T) where Y is a compact space and T a homeomorphism of X onto an everywhere dense subset of Y; such a couple is called a *compactification* of X.

Conversely, let us start from a compactification (Y, T) and denote by A the algebra of the functions $g \circ T$ where $g \in \mathscr{C}(Y)$; its elements are continuous and bounded; the mapping $g \to g \circ T$ of $\mathscr{C}(Y)$ onto A is an isometric isomorphism and hence A is a closed subalgebra of

$\mathscr{C}^\infty(X)$; the other properties can trivially be verified. If we start from a subalgebra A satisfying (i) to (iv) and if we successively make the two constructions above, it is clear that we find A; if we start from a compactification (Y, T) and if we make the two constructions in reverse order, we obtain a compactification (Y', T') which is equivalent to (Y, T), meaning by that that there exists a homeomorphism S of Y onto Y' for which the following diagram is commutative

$$\begin{array}{ccc} & & Y \\ & \overset{T}{\nearrow} & \\ X & & \Big\downarrow S \\ & \underset{T'}{\searrow} & \\ & & Y' \end{array} \qquad (1)$$

In short

Proposition 8.1. The construction described in the beginning of this section establishes a bijective correspondence between the subalgebras of $\mathscr{C}^\infty(X)$ satisfying ((i), . . ., (iv)) and the compactifications of X, on condition that two compactifications which are equivalent in the above sense are identified.

This correspondence is order-preserving in the following sense: we say that $(Y', T') \leqq (Y, T)$ if there exists a continuous mapping S of Y into Y' for which the diagram (1) is commutative; (Y, T) and (Y', T') being now the compactifications corresponding to A and A', we get $(Y', T') \leqq (Y, T)$ if and only if $A' \subset A$ (the "only if" part is trivial; for the "if" part, use the properties of the spectra of the sub-C^*-algebras described at the end of § 7.2).

Examples. (X denotes a completely regular topological space).

1. Because of what has just been said, the algebra $\mathscr{C}^\infty(X)$, being the largest of the algebras satisfying (i), . . ., (iv), gives rise to the largest compactification, called the *Stone-Čech compactification*; more precisely, denoting by βX the compactification obtained in this way and considering X as immersed in βX, we can say that any continuous mapping of X into a compact space extends to βX, obviously in a unique manner; this compactification is thus the solution of a readily formulated universal problem (cf. [2], § 3).

2. Let $\mathscr{F}$ be a filter on X without adherent point and A the subset of $\mathscr{C}^\infty(X)$ composed of the functions having a limit with respect to

$\mathscr{F}$; A is a subalgebra satisfying (i), . . ., (iv) (easy); in this way we obtain a compactification containing the character $f \to \lim_F f$. For instance if X is locally compact and if $\mathscr{F}$ is the filter generated by the complements of the compact sets, we obtain the Alexandrov compactification.

3. We mention a related theory: let G be a topological group; the almost-periodic functions on G form a subalgebra A of $\mathscr{C}^\infty(G)$ which satisfies (i), (ii), (iii) but not necessarily (iv); we then have a continuous mapping T, which is not necessarily injective, of G into $\hat{A}$ and $T(G)$ is again everywhere dense in $\hat{A}$; $\hat{A}$ can be endowed with a compact group structure such that T is a morphism; if T is injective, one says that G is "representable in a compact group"; but even in this case T is not necessarily bicontinuous; this is the case for $\mathfrak{R}$.

Exercises

Let X be a completely regular topological space and βX its Stone-Čech compactification.

1. X is open in βX if and only if X is locally compact.

2. βX is connected if and only if X is. In the following exercises we suppose X is *discrete*.

3. βX is totally discontinuous; there is no point of $\beta X - X$ which admits a countable fundamental system of neighbourhoods.

4. Let $\mathscr{F}$ be an ultra-filter on X; the mapping $f \to \lim_F f$ is a character of $\mathscr{C}^\infty(X)$, say χ_F; the mapping $\mathscr{F} \to \chi_F$ is a bijection of the set of ultra-filters onto βX.

(Note that if X is not supposed to be discrete, one can still make an analogous theory on condition that the ultrafilters be replaced by other filters, called "completely regular maximal" filters (cf. [6], § 1, ex. 8).

§ 8.2. *Spectral theory of normal operators in Hilbert spaces*

(See von Neumann Algebras, chap. III, § 5).

no. 1. *Commutative C*-algebras of operators in Hilbert spaces.*

Let H be a complex Hilbert space and A a commutative closed self-adjoint subalgebra, containing I, of $\mathscr{L}(H)$; we know that A is a

C^*-algebra and that the Gelfand transformation is an isomorphism of A onto $\mathscr{C}(\hat{A})$; the inverse mapping will be denoted by $f \to T_f$ (this mapping is a measure on $\hat{A}$ with values in $\mathscr{L}(H)$); we will extend it to a larger class of functions, namely the algebra $\mathscr{B}(\hat{A})$ of the bounded Borel complex functions on $\hat{A}$ – – – which at the same time will considerably improve the functional calculus in A; we say immediately that the operators obtained in this way no longer necessarily belong to A, but to the von Neumann algebra generated by A, or "bicommutant" A'' of A (see [9] or [13]).

Spectral measures

For all x and all $y \in H$ we define a complex-valued measure $\mu_{x,y}$ on $\hat{A}$ by

$$\mu_{x,y}(f) = (T_f x \mid y) \quad \forall f \in \mathscr{C}(\hat{A});$$

these measures have some readily verified properties

– $\|\mu_{x,y}\| \leqq \|x\| \cdot \|y\|$

– $\mu_{x,y} = \overline{\mu_{y,x}}$ which means that $\mu_{x,y}(f) = \overline{\mu_{y,x}(\bar{f})}$

– $\mu_{T_g x, T_h y} = g\bar{h}\mu_{x,y}$ which means that $\mu_{T_g x, T_h y}(f) = \mu_{x,y}(g\bar{h}f)$

– $\mu_{Sx,y} = \mu_{x,S^*y}$ for all $S \in A'$ = commutant of A.

Each measure $\mu_{x,y}$ extends to $\mathscr{B}(\hat{A})$ and for all $b \in \mathscr{B}(\hat{A})$ we also have

$$|\mu_{x,y}(b)| \leqq \|b\| \cdot \|x\| \cdot \|y\|;$$

$\mu_{x,y}(b)$ is hence, with respect to x and y, a continuous sesquilinear form; we can define the

Extension of the mapping $f \to T_f$

by the formula

$$\mu_{x,y}(b) = (T_b x \mid y) \qquad b \in \mathscr{B}(\hat{A}) \tag{1}$$

where T_b is an element of $\mathscr{L}(H)$ satisfying $\|T_b\| \leqq \|b\|$; note the relation

$$\|T_b x\|^2 = \mu_{x,x}(b\bar{b}) \qquad \forall x \in H. \tag{2}$$

From (1) we see that the mapping $b \to T_b$ is linear; it has moreover the following properties

- $T_{\bar{b}} = T_b^*$
- $T_b \in A''$
- $\mu_{T_b x, y} = b \cdot \mu_{x,y}$
- $T_{bb'} = T_b \cdot T_{b'}$

which are readily verified; we indicate the method by considering the first one; for x and $y \in H$ we have

$$(T_{\bar{b}} x \mid y) = \mu_{x,y}(\bar{b}) = \overline{\mu_{y,x}(b)} = \overline{(T_b y \mid x)} = (T_b^* x \mid y);$$

in short

Proposition 8.2. The isomorphism $f \to T_f$ of $\mathscr{C}(\hat{A})$ onto A extends to a continuous morphism of $*$-algebras of $\mathscr{B}(\hat{A})$ into A'', characterized by the formula (1).

Remark 8.1. Since A is commutative we have $A \subset A'' \subset A'$ and A'' is also commutative; in fact one shows that the above-mentioned extension maps $\mathscr{B}(\hat{A})$ *onto* A'' – – – at least if H is separable.

no. 2. *Spectral decomposition of the normal operators*

Let T be a normal element of $\mathscr{L}(H)$ ("normal" means that $TT^* = T^*T$), X its spectrum in $\mathscr{L}(H)$, A the commutative C^*-algebra generated by T.

Lemma 8.1. We have $X = \mathrm{sp}_A\, T$.

We must show that if $T - \lambda I$ is not invertible in A, it is not invertible in $\mathscr{L}(H)$; now $(T - \lambda I)\,(T^* - \bar{\lambda} I)$ is not invertible on A, i.e.

$$-\lambda\bar{\lambda} \in \mathrm{sp}_A\,(TT^* - \bar{\lambda}T - \lambda T^*);$$

since the element in parantheses is hermitian, its spectrum is real, hence equal to its boundary; from § 1.6, $(T - \lambda I)\,(T^* - \bar{\lambda} I)$ is not invertible in $\mathscr{L}(H)$ and it follows readily that $T - \lambda I$ is not invertible either.

Q. E. D.

From what was said at the end of § 7.2, we can identify $\hat{A}$ with X, a subset of $\mathfrak{C}$; the study of no. 1 provides a continuous morphism

$b \to T_b$ of $\mathscr{B}(X)$ into $\mathscr{L}(H)$ and the image of the function $z \to z$ is actually T; if in particular b is the characteristic function of a Borel subset Z of X, T_b is an orthogonal projection operator denoted by E_z and called *spectral projection operator* of T; since the function $z \to z$ is a uniform limit of linear combinations of characteristic functions, we have the

Proposition 8.3. Any normal continuous linear operator in a Hilbert space is a limit, for the norm topology, of linear combinations of spectral projection operators.

Notations. For all $f \in \mathscr{B}(X)$ one often writes $f(T)$ instead of T_f; on the other hand the following symbolic notations, derived from (1), are often used:

$$(f(T)\, x \mid y) = \iint f(z) \cdot (E(\mathrm{d}u \cdot \mathrm{d}v)\, x \mid y) \qquad z = u + iv$$

$$f(T) = \iint f(z) \cdot E(\mathrm{d}u \cdot \mathrm{d}v). \tag{3}$$

Characteristic values. It is not difficult to see that an element of X is a characteristic values of T if and only if the spectral projection operator $E_{\{\lambda\}}$ is non-zero; and that the corresponding subspace is then the characteristic subspace corresponding to the characteristic value λ.

Particular cases. If T is *hermitian,* its spectrum X is real; for any real number λ we denote by E_λ the projection operator corresponding to the set $]-\infty, \lambda]$ which allows us to replace (3) by

$$f(T) = \int f(\lambda) \cdot \mathrm{d}E_\lambda$$

and in particular

$$T = \int \lambda \cdot \mathrm{d}E_\lambda .$$

If T is *unitary,* X is contained in the circle $|z| = 1$ and one usually writes

$$T = \int e^{i\lambda} \cdot \mathrm{d}E_\lambda .$$

Remark 8.2. An analogous theory can be constructed for certain operators, called "spectral" operators, in Banach spaces (cf. [18], § 17,5); one of the main problems of the theory consists of the generalization of Proposition 8.3 – – – what obviously is not allowed by the functional calculus described in Chapter III; see also [36].

no. 3. *Study of certain non-continuous operators*

We will use the notations of no. 1; we consider a not necessarily bounded complex Borel function b on $\hat{A}$ and indicate briefly the definition of the operator T_b, which is in general not continuous.

The formula (2) leads to the choice, as domain of definition of T_b, of the set H' of x such that b has integrable square for $\mu_{x,x}$; before continuing it is useful to give another characterization of H'; for any integer $n \geqq 0$, let us call Y_n the set of $\chi \in \hat{A}$ such that $n \leqq |b(\chi)| < n + 1$, b_n the restriction of b to Y_n and, for all $x \in H$, let us set $x_n = E_{Y_n}(x)$ we note that the E_{Y_n} are orthogonal mutually and have sum equal to I; we get

$$\mu_{x,x}(b_n\bar{b}_n) = \|T_{b_n}(x)\|^2$$

hence H' is the set of x such that $\sum \|T_{b_n}(x)\|^2 < +\infty$; we see thus that H' is a *vector subspace which is everywhere dense* in H.

For all $x \in H'$ we can set $T_b x = \sum T_{b_n}(x)$ and we have

$$\|T_b x\|^2 = \sum \|T_{b_n}(x)\|^2 = \sum \mu_{x,x}(b_n\bar{b}_n) = \mu_{x,x}(b\bar{b});$$

now if $y \in H$ we have

$$(T_b x \mid y) = \sum (T_{b_n}(x) \mid y) = \sum \mu_{x,y}(b_n) = \mu_{x,y}(b).$$

Then it is clear that we can define the operator $T_{\bar{b}}$ on the same subspace H' and that we have, for x and $y \in H'$

$$(T_b x \mid y) = (x \mid T_{\bar{b}} y);$$

one shows that in fact $T_{\bar{b}}$ defined in this way is *exactly the adjoint* T_b^* of T_b, whence one deduces that T_b is *closed*, and even *self-adjoint if b is real.*

Usually one also uses the notation

$$T_b = \int b(\lambda) \cdot \mathrm{d}E_\lambda$$

and one characterizes H' as the set of x such that

$$\int |b(\lambda)|^2 \cdot \mathrm{d}\|E_\lambda x\|^2 < +\infty.$$

Remark 8.3. The results of nos. 1,2,3 become clearer if H is the integral of a measurable field of Hilbert spaces on $\hat{A}$, say

$$H = \int^{\oplus} H(\chi) \cdot \mathrm{d}\nu(\chi)$$

condition which we can always suppose realized if H is separable (see [9], Chapter II, § 6 or [13], Chapter III, § 5); because an element x of H is then a field $\chi \to x(\chi)$ which is square integrable; each measure $\mu_{x,y}$ is the product of ν by the function $\chi \to (x(\chi) \mid y(\chi))$; for any function $b \in \mathscr{B}(\hat{A})$, T_b is the operator of "multiplication" by b which makes the field $b(\chi) \cdot x(\chi)$ correspond to each field $x(\chi)$; finally if b is non-bounded and Borel, H' is the set of x such that the field $b(\chi) \cdot x(\chi)$ is square integrable.

no. 4. *One-parameter semi-groups of hermitian operators*

We call thus any mapping π of $\mathfrak{R}_+^*$ into the set of hermitian continuous linear operators of a Hilbert space H, which is continuous for the strong topology (i.e. each mapping $s \to \pi(s) \cdot x$, where $x \in H$, is strongly continuous) and satisfying $\pi(s+t) = \pi(s) \cdot \pi(t)$. If $\pi(s)$ is zero for some s it is zero for all s, and we will exclude this case. It is easy to see that the function $s \to \|\pi(s)\|$ is lower semi-continuous and that the function $s \to \log \|\pi(s)\|$ is sub-additive; it follows from the properties of sub-additive functions that there exists a number

$$u = \lim_{s \to \infty} \|\pi(s)\|^{1/s} = \inf \|\pi(s)\|^{1/s};$$

in particular

$$u = \lim \|\pi(n)\|^{1/n} = \lim \|\pi(1)^n\|^{1/n} = \|\pi(1)\| > 0$$

let us set $u = e^v$; we then get

$$\|\pi(s)\| = \lim \|\pi(ns)\|^{1/n} = e^{sv}.$$

Denote by A the commutative C^*-algebra generated by the $\pi(s)$ and I; corresponding to π there is a mapping $s \to \widehat{\pi(s)}$ of $\mathfrak{R}_+^*$ into $\mathscr{C}(\hat{A}, \mathfrak{R})$ satisfying

$$\widehat{\pi(s+t)} = \widehat{\pi(s)} \cdot \widehat{\pi(t)}$$

$$\|\pi(s)\| = e^{sv};$$

let $\chi \in \hat{A}$; as we did earlier we see that if $\widehat{\pi(s)}\,(\chi)$ is zero for some s, it is zero for all s; denote by F the (closed) set of the corresponding χ and $G = \hat{A} - F$; one shows that for all $\chi \in G$, $\widehat{\pi(s)}\,(\chi)$ is of form $e^{sg(\chi)}$

where g is a real function; it is continuous since $g(\chi) = \log \widehat{\pi(1)}(\chi)$, and satisfies $g(\chi) \leqq v$; in short, we have

$$\widehat{\pi(s)}(\chi) = \begin{cases} 0 & \text{if } \chi \in F \\ e^{sg(\chi)} & \text{if } \chi \in G. \end{cases}$$

It is then clear that for all s we have

$$\pi(s)E_G = E_G\pi(s) = \pi(s)$$

in other words, $\pi(s)$ leaves the subspace $E_G(H)$ invariant and is zero in the orthogonal subspace; moreover $\pi(s)$ tends strongly towards E_G for $s \to 0$; indeed, if $x \in E_G(H)$ we have

$$\|\pi(s) \cdot x - x\|^2 = \mu_{x,x}(\widehat{\pi(s)}^2) - 2\mu_{x,x}(\widehat{\pi(s)}) + \mu_{x,x}(G)$$

and this tends to 0 according to the Lebesgue theorem.

Finally denote by g' the function g extended by 0 on F; the operator (in general it is not continuous) $T_{g'}$ is called the *infinitesimal generator* of the semi-group π; one shows that

$$T_{g'}x = \lim 1/s \cdot (\pi(s) \cdot x - E_G x)$$

for all x such that $T_{g'}x$ is defined; in symbols, we write

$$\pi(s) = E_G \cdot \exp(sT_{g'}).$$

§ 8.3. *Boolean algebras*

This section is not strictly speaking an application, but rather a parallel study, where we will prove some classical results concerning the structure of Boolean algebras.

Let A be a Boolean algebra; we denote by 0 and e its smallest and largest elements, by $\wedge$, $\vee$ and $'$ the operations of lower bound, upper bound and complementation; we endow A with an algebra structure over the field $\mathscr{K} = \{0, 1\}$ by setting

$$x + y = (x \wedge y') \vee (x' \wedge y)$$

$$xy = x \wedge y;$$

for this structure, every element is idempotent and A has characteristic 2; e is the only invertible element, hence if A is a field A is isomorphic to $\mathcal{K}$ (theorem of Gelfand-Mazur!). A subset I of A distinct from A is an ideal if and only if it has the following properties:

$$x \text{ and } y \in I \Rightarrow x \vee y \in I$$

$$x \in I \text{ and } y \in A \Rightarrow x \wedge y \in I$$

(one also says that $A - I$ is a "filter"); I is a maximal ideal if and only if, for all $x \in A$, we have $x \in I$ or $x' \in I$.

We call a "character" of A any non-zero $\mathcal{K}$-algebra morphism of A into $\mathcal{K}$; in other words a character is an order-preserving mapping of A into $\{0, 1\}$; it is easy to see that there is a bijective correspondence between maximal ideals and characters and that the intersection of the kernels of the characters is reduced to $\{0\}$. The set $\hat{A}$ of the characters, endowed with the topology of simple convergence, is compact and totally discontinuous (the functions $\hat{x}, x \in A$, only assume the values 0 and 1!); we already know that the Gelfand transformation is injective; it is surjective, because, as can readily be seen, any separating subalgebra of $\mathcal{C}(\hat{A}, \mathcal{K})$ is equal to $\mathcal{C}(\hat{A}, \mathcal{K})$; in short

Proposition 8.4. (Stone). Every Boolean algebra is isomorphic to the Boolean algebra of the open and closed subsets of a totally discontinuous compact space.

We now start from a totally discontinuous compact space X and denote by Y the spectrum of the Boolean algebra $\mathcal{C}(X, \mathcal{K})$; as in § 6.1 we have an injective continuous mapping T of X into Y; to show that it is surjective, we take a maximal ideal I of $\mathcal{C}(X, \mathcal{K})$; if I were not contained in any ideal Ker $T(x)$, there would exist, for all $x \in X$, an open-and-closed set E_x belonging to I and containing x; we could extract a finite covering from it, and I would contain X; hence I is contained in an ideal Ker $T(x)$, and is hence equal to it. Thus we have the

Proposition 8.5. There is a bijective correspondence between Boolean algebras and totally discontinuous compact spaces, associating its spectrum to each Boolean algebra and to each totally discontinuous compact space X the Boolean algebra $\mathcal{C}(X, \mathcal{K})$ of its open and closed subsets.

Application to certain C. B. A. Let A be a commutative C^*-algebra with unit and A_1 the Boolean algebra of the idempotent elements of A; under the Gelfand transformation of A onto $\mathscr{C}(\hat{A})$, the Boolean algebra of the open and closed subsets of $\hat{A}$ corresponds to A_1; if A is generated by A_1, $\hat{A}$ is totally discontinuous and is at the same time the spectrum of A_1; this applies in particular to example (g) (the idempotents of $L^\infty(X, \mu)$ are the μ-measurable subsets defined up to μ-negligeable subsets); even more particularly, if we take X to be discrete, we find again the result of § 8.1, ex. 4.

APPENDIX I

POLYNOMIALLY AND RATIONALLY CONVEX COMPACT SUBSETS

A compact subset X of a space $\mathfrak{C}^n$ is said to be *polynomially* (resp. *rationally*) *convex* if for each point $z^0 \in \mathfrak{C}^n - X$ we can find a polynomial (resp. a rational fraction which is regular on $X \cup \{z^0\}$) f satisfying

$$|f(z^0)| > \sup_{z \in X} |f(z)|; \tag{1}$$

this is equivalent to saying that X is compact and defined by conditions of the form $|f_i(x)| \leqq k_i$ where the f_i are polynomials (resp. rational fractions regular on X). It is clear that polynomially convex implies rationally convex.

Let X be a compact subset of $\mathfrak{C}^n$; the set X' of points z^0 satisfying

$$|f(z^0)| \leqq \sup_{z \in X} |f(z)|$$

for every polynomial (resp. every rational fraction regular on X) is compact, polynomially (resp. rationally) convex and contains X and it is the smallest set with these properties; it is called the *polynomially* (resp. *rationally*) *convex hull* of X.

In the case $n = 1$, every compact subset is rationally convex, because (1) is satisfied by suitably translating the function $z \to 1/(z - z^0)$; a compact subset X is polynomially convex if and only if $\mathfrak{C} - X$ is connected (Corollary 2.3); on the other hand, for $n > 1$ there is no topological characterization of polynomially convex compact subsets.

Every polynomially convex compact subset $X \subset \mathfrak{C}^n$ admits a fundamental system of polynomially convex compact neighbourhoods.

Indeed, X admits a compact neighbourhood Y defined by conditions $|z_i| \leqq h_i$; then let U be an arbitrary open neighbourhood of X; for each $t \in Y - U \cap Y$ there exists a polynomial f_t satisfying

$$|f_t(t)| > \sup_{z \in X} |f_t(z)| = k_t;$$

t admits an open neighbourhood V_t such that

$$z \in V_t \Rightarrow |f_t(z)| > k_t + \varepsilon_t \quad \text{where} \quad \varepsilon_t > 0;$$

$Y - U \cap Y$ is convered by a finite number of V_t, say $V_{t_1}, \ldots, V_{t_q}$; then U contains the polynomially convex compact neighbourhood of X defined by the conditions

$$|f_{t_j}(z)| \leqq k_{t_j} + \varepsilon_{t_j} \qquad j = 1, \ldots, q$$
$$|z_i| \leqq h_i \qquad i = 1, \ldots, n.$$

(Analogous result for rationally convex compact subsets).

APPENDIX II

THE ALGEBRAS $\mathcal{O}(U)$ AND $\mathcal{O}(K)$

(See Topological Algebras and Holomorphic Functions § 1.2, 1.7 and App. I.)

For any open subset U of $\mathfrak{C}^n$ we denote by $\mathcal{O}(U)$ the set of complex functions holomorphic on U, endowed with the topology of compact convergence; this topology is not defined by a norm, but by a sequence of semi-norms; as a topological vector space, $\mathcal{O}(U)$ is a Frechet space; $\mathcal{O}(U)$ is a *topological* algebra in the sense that the mapping $(f, g) \to fg$ is continuous.

Let now K be a compact subset of $\mathfrak{C}^n$; we denote by $\mathcal{O}(K)$ the sum set of the $\mathcal{O}(U)$ --- where U is a variable open neighbourhood of K --- where we identify two functions $f \in \mathcal{O}(U)$ and $f' \in \mathcal{O}(U')$ if they coincide on a third neighbourhood $U'' \subset U \cap U'$ (or, as is also said, if they *have the same germ in the neighbourhood of* K); $\mathcal{O}(K)$ is naturally endowed with an algebra structure; we endow it with a topology in the following manner; for each U we denote by T_U the canonical mapping $\mathcal{O}(U) \to \mathcal{O}(K)$ which associates its germ to each function of $\mathcal{O}(U)$; we take on $\mathcal{O}(K)$ the finest locally convex topology for which all the T_U are continuous; this topology, called the *inductive limit*, has the following remarkable property (cf. [7], Chapter II, § 2, no. 2): a linear mapping S of $\mathcal{O}(K)$ into a locally convex topological vector space is continuous if and only if all the mappings $S \circ T_U$ are continuous.

It is possible to describe the topology of $\mathcal{O}(K)$ by specifying somewhat the neighbourhoods U; for every integer $n > 0$ let U_n be the set of points whose distance from K is $< 1/n$; the U_n constitute a fundamental system of neighbourhoods of K; since each connected component of U_n meets K, the mapping T_U is injective; on the other hand we have $\overline{U}_n \subset U_{n-1}$; let A_n be the set of functions continuous on $\overline{U}_n$ and holomorphic on U_n; endowed with the norm of uniform convergence on $\overline{U}_n$, A_n becomes a Banach algebra; we get obvious continuous mappings.

$$\mathcal{O}(U_{n-1}) \rightarrow A_n \rightarrow \mathcal{O}(U_n);$$

consequently the topology of $\mathcal{O}(K)$ is also the inductive limit corresponding to the canonical mappings $R_n : A_n \rightarrow \mathcal{O}(K)$; $\mathcal{O}(K)$ now appears as an *inductive limit of Banach algebras.*

We obtain a fundamental system of neighbourhoods of O in $\mathcal{O}(K)$ by taking a sequence $k_n > 0$, then, for each n, the ball B_{k_n} with center 0 and radius k_n in A_n, and finally the convexe hull of the set $\bigcup R_n\,(B_{k_n})$ (note that 0 admits no countable fundamental system of neighbourhoods, or, in other words, that $\mathcal{O}(K)$ is not metrizable). It is then easy to see that $\mathcal{O}(K)$ is a *topological algebra*; we mention that it is complete and has continuous inverse.

INDEX

BIBLIOGRAPHY

Reference Books

[1] F. Bingen – J. Tits – L. Waelbroeck. Séminaire sur les Algèbres de Banach. Université libre de Bruxelles. 1962–1963.
[2] N. Bourbaki. Théorie des Ensembles, ch. IV.
[3] N. Bourbaki. Algèbre, ch. II.
[4] N. Bourbaki. Algèbre, ch. VIII.
[5] N. Bourbaki. Algèbre Commutative, ch. II.
[6] N. Bourbaki. Topologie Générale, ch. IX, 2° édition.
[7] N. Bourbaki. Espaces Vectoriels Topologiques, ch. I et II.
[8] N. Bourbaki. Intégration, ch. V.
[9] J. Dixmier. Algèbres de von Neumann. Gauthier-Villars, 1957.
[10] B. A. Fuks. Introduction to the Theory of Analytic Functions of Several Complex Variables. Transl. of Math. Monographs, vol. 8, 1963.
[11] I. M. Gelfand – D. A. Raikov – G. E. Chilov. Kommutative normierte Algebren. VEB, Berlin, 1964.
[12] L. Gillman – M. Jerison. Rings of Continuous Functions. Van Nostrand, 1960.
[13] A. Guichardet. Algèbres de von Neumann. (Cours multigraphié, Poitiers) (part II of this book).
[14] P. R. Halmos. Lectures on Boolean Algebras. Van Nostrand, 1963.
[15] E. Hille – R. S. Phillips. Functional Analysis and Semi-Groups. Amer. Math. Soc. Coll. Publ., 1957.
[16] K. Hoffman. Banach Spaces of Analytic Functions. Prentice-Hall, 1962.
[17] L. H. Loomis. An Introduction to Abstract Harmonic Analysis. Van Nostrand, 1953.
[18] M. A. Naimark. Normed Rings. Noordhoff, 1959.
[19] C. E. Rickart. General Theory of Banach Algebras. Van Nostrand, 1960.
[20] L. Waelbroeck. Théorie des Algèbres de Banach et des Algèbres localement convexes. Université de Montréal, 1962.

Reference Papers

[21] R. Arens. The problem of locally-A functions in a commutative Banach algebra A. Trans. Amer. Math. Soc., t. 104, 1962, p. 24–36.
[22] S. Bergmann. Über ausgezeichnete Randflächen in der Theorie der Funktionen von zwei komplexen Veränderlichen. Math. Annalen, t. 104, 1931, p. 611–636.

[23] E. Bishop. Aminimal boundary for function algebras. Pac. J. Math., t. 9, 1959, p. 629–642.
[24] E. Bishop – K. de Leeuw. The representation of linear functionals by measures on sets of extreme points. Ann. Inst. Fourier, t. 9, 1959, p. 305–331.
[25] N. Dunford. Spectral operators. Pac. J. Math., t. 4, 1954, p. 321–354.
[26] O. Forster. Banach Algebren stetiger Funktionen auf kompakten Räumen. Math. Zeits., t. 81, 1963, p. 1–34.
[27] K. Hoffman. Minimal boundaries for analytic polyedra. Rend. Circ. Mat. Palermo, t. 9, 1960, p. 147–160.
[28] K. Hoffman – H. Rossi. The minimal boundary for an analytic polyedron. Pac. J. Math. t. 12, 1962, p. 1347–1353.
[29] K. Hoffman – J. Wermer. A characterization of $C(X)$. Pac. J. Math., t. 12, 1962, p. 941–944.
[30] E. Kallin. A non local function algebra. Proc. Nat. Acad. Sci., t. 49, 1963, p. 821.
[31] R. McKissick. A non trivial normal sup norm algebra. Bull. Amer. Math. Soc., t. 69, 1963, p. 391–395.
[32] P. Malliavin. Sur l'impossibilité de la synthèse spectrale sur la droite. C. R. Acad. Sci., t. 248, 1959, p. 2155–2157.
[33] S. N. Mergelyan. Uniform approximations to functions of a complex variable. Transl. Amer. Math. Soc., series 1, vol. 3.
[34] H. Rossi. The Local Maximum Modulus Principle. Ann. Math., t. 71, 1960, p. 1–11.
[34′] H. Rossi. Holomorphically convex sets in several complex variables. Ann. Math., t. 74, 1961, p. 470.
[35] H. L. Royden. Function Algebras. Bull. Amer. Math. Soc., t. 69, 1963, p. 281–298.
[36] P. Saphar. Contribution à l'étude des applications linéaires dans un espace de Banach. Bull. Soc. Math. France. t. 92, 1964, p. 363–384.
[37] G. Stolzenberg. The maximal ideal space of the functions locally in a function algebra. Proc. Amer. Math. Soc., t. 14, 1963, p. 342–345.
[38] N. T. Varopoulos. Sur les formes positives d'une algèbre de Banach. C. R. Acad. Sci., t. 258, 1964, p. 2465–2467.
[39′] J. Wermer. Banach Algebras of Analytic Functions. Advances in Math. t. 1, 1961.
[39] J. Wermer. Uniform approximation and maximal ideal spaces. Bull. Amer. Math. Soc., t. 68, 1962, p. 298–304.
[40] H. Whitney. On ideals of differentiable functions. Amer. J. Math., t. 70, 1948, p. 635–658.

VON NEUMANN ALGEBRAS

CONTENTS

INTRODUCTION

The theory of von Neumann Algebras, besides its inherent interest --- it leads to a satisfactory classification of the objects under study --- is useful in other fields of Functional Analysis, namely for the study of C^*-algebras as well as of the unitary representations of locally compact groups (for instance of solvable Lie groups); we also mention that it seems to play a role in Theoretical Physics in the axiomatization of Quantum Field Theory and in finding representations of the commutation relations.

The present treatise closely follows that of [1]; however we amputated that treatise of a rather large number of concepts and results, feeling that a non-specialist reader or a possible user of the theory could do without them; thus in Chapter II we do not mention ultra-strong and ultra-weak topologies on $\mathscr{L}(H)$, nothwithstanding their undoubted advantage of being more intrinsic for von Neumann algebras than the strong and weak topologies; and in Chapter III we suppose that all the spaces, topological or Hilbert, have countable bases, in order to avoid complications (which are sometimes, we must admit, only complications of terminology); also in Chapter IV we assume the main result of the theory of Hilbert Algebras (the commutation theorem) and omit the classification of von Neumann algebras other than the factors.

We thought it useful to start the treatise by examining a very particular case: that where the Hilbert space has finite dimension; this allows us to get familiarized first with the algebraic aspect of the question before dealing with the difficulties due to the topology and the measure; it is perhaps not completely senseless to speak thus of a geometrical aspect of the question: operators in a direct sum or in a tensor product, operators and algebras induced in a stable subspace. Moreover several results pertaining to this particular case can be transposed more or less without alterations to the general case, to such an extent that we sometimes omitted the proofs.

In the beginning of Chapter II we have grouped together some concepts and results which will be used later, concerning Spectral

Theory and polar decomposition, an essential tool for the study of traces.

Chapter III is devoted to Reduction Theory, whose main instrument is the theory of Measure; we use the latter in the frame of locally compact topological spaces, even though the topology occurs rather artificially in this question and is in any case just barely intrinsic in the results; in fact we could have replaced the topology by a much weaker type of structure: the Borel structures, standard in this case, described by G. W. Mackey; we would have obtained results entirely parallel to those of Chapter III; moreover in Theorem 3.3 we would have constructed a standard Borel space, unique up to isomorphism; however we preferred topological structures, more generally known than Borel structures. The main results of this chapter, the structure of commutative von Neumann algebras and the decomposition of an arbitrary von Neumann algebra into factors, are essentially rather analogous to those of Chapter I.

Finally, in Chapter IV, we approach the study of the structure of the factors in a roundabout way by first studying the traces, first considered as functions defined on the positive elements, with finite or infinite positive real values, and then as linear forms defined on ideals; we deduce a classification of the factors and finally specify the structure of each type of factor by examinning the values assumed by the traces on the projection operators.

CHAPTER I

THE CASE OF FINITE-DIMENSIONAL HILBERT SPACES

§ 1. *Preliminaries*

1. *Vectors, subspaces, operators*

We denote by H a complex Hilbert space of finite dimension n, or again the vector space composed of the sequences of n complex numbers $x = (x_1, \ldots, x_n)$ and endowed with the *scalar product*

$$(x \mid y) = x_1\bar{y}_1 + \cdots x_n\bar{y}_n;$$

any vector x then admits a *norm* $\|x\| = (x \mid x)^{\frac{1}{2}}$.

Two vectors x and y are *orthogonal* if $(x \mid y) = 0$ (we write $x \perp y$); two vector subspaces X and Y are *orthogonal* if every vector of X is orthogonal to every vector of Y; any vector subspace X admits an *orthogonal complement* $H \ominus X$ --- the set of vectors orthogonal to X. If $X_1, \ldots, X_p$ are subspaces which are orthogonal two by two, their *Hilbert sum*, denoted by $X_1 \oplus \ldots \oplus X_p$ or $\bigoplus_{i=1}^{p} X_i$, is the subspace generated by $X_1, \ldots, X_p$.

Every linear operator T admits an adjoint T^* defined by

$$(T^*x \mid y) = (x \mid Ty) \qquad \forall x, y \in H;$$

if T is represented by a matrix $(a_{i,j})$, T^* is represented by the matrix $(b_{i,j})$ where $b_{i,j} = \bar{a}_{i,j}$ · T is *hermitian* if $T^* = T$; T is *positive* ($T \geqq 0$) if $(Tx \mid x) \geqq 0$ $\forall x \in H$; T is then hermitian; for every operator T, T^*T and TT^* are positive.

An operator T is *unitary* if $(Tx \mid Ty) = (x \mid y)$ $\forall x, y$, which is equivalent to $T^*T = TT^* = 1$.

The set $\mathscr{L}(H)$ of linear operators is a $*$-*algebra*, that is to say, it is an algebra over the complex field with an operation $T \to T^*$ satisfying the following axioms:

(i) $$(T + S)^* = T^* + S^*$$

(ii) $$(kT)^* = \bar{k}T^*$$

(iii) $$(TS)^* = S^*T^*$$

(iv) $$T^{**} = T.$$

It admits moreover a unit element denoted by 1 and a *norm* defined by
$$\|T\| = \sup \|Tx\| \quad \text{for} \quad \|x\| \leqq 1$$
and satisfying

(v) $$\|T^*T\| = \|T\|^2.$$

2. *Projection operators*

If X is a vector subspace of H, we denote by P_X the *orthogonal projection operator* on X, i.e. the linear operator associating to each vector x the vector y of X such that $x - y \perp X$; the orthogonal projection operators (often simply called *projection operators*) are hermitian and idempotent linear operators, i.e. $T^2 = T$. Two projection operators P_X and P_Y are *orthogonal* if X and Y are, or again if $P_XP_Y = P_YP_X = 0$; we then have $P_{X \oplus Y} = P_X + P_Y$; we will often denote by the same letter a projection operator and the corresponding subspace.

Let X be a subspace, T an operator; the following properties are equivalent:

- X is stable under T and T^*
- X and $H \ominus X$ are stable under T
- P_X commutes with T
- P_X commutes with T^*;

the restriction of T to X is then an operator in X, called the *induced* operator and denoted by T_X.

3. *Decomposition theorem*

a) Every operator T can be uniquely set in the form $T_1 + iT_2$, where T_1 and T_2 are hermitian.

b) every positive operator T admits a unique positive square root, denoted by $T^{\frac{1}{2}}$, which commutes with every operator commuting with T.

c) *Polar decomposition.* Every operator T can we written as $T = U\,|T|$ where U is unitary and $|T| = (T^*T)^{\frac{1}{2}}$.

d) *Spectral decomposition.* Every hermitian operator is a linear combination of projection operators, say $T = \sum \lambda_i P_i$, where λ_i are distinct real numbers called the characteristic values of T, and P_i are projection operators, orthogonal two by two, on subspaces called the *characteristic subspaces*; the *spectral projection operators* of T are the sums of projectors P_i. If f is a complex function of a real variable we can define $f(T)$ by $f(T) = \sum\limits_i f(\lambda_i) P_i$; $f(T)$ commutes with any operator which commutes with T.

4. *Operators in a Hilbert sum*

Suppose H is a Hilbert sum of subspaces $H_1, \ldots, H_r$ and set $P_i = P_{H_i}$ every $x \in H$ can be written uniquely as $\sum x_i$ where $x_i \in H_i$; let T be an operator in H and let $T_{i,j}$ be the restriction of $P_i T$ to H_j; we have

$$(Tx)_i = P_i Tx = P_i T\left(\sum_j x_j\right) = \sum_j P_i T x_j = \sum_j T_{i,j} x_j$$

We say that T is *represented by the matrix* $(T_{i,j})$ whose element $T_{i,j}$ is a linear mapping of H_j into H_i. We get the relations

$$(T + S)_{i,j} = T_{i,j} + S_{i,j}$$

$$(TS)_{i,j} = \sum_k T_{i,k} S_{k,j}$$

$$(T^*)_{i,j} = T^*_{i,j}.$$

5. *Operators in a tensor product*

Let $H = H_1 \otimes H_2$, where the scalar product is defined by

$$(x_1 \otimes x_2 \mid y_1 \otimes y_2) = (x_1 \mid y_1)\,(x_2 \mid y_2);$$

if $f_1, \ldots, f_m$ and $e_1, \ldots, e_n$ are orthonormal bases of H_1 and H_2, $(f_j \otimes e_i)$ is an orthonormal basis of H; H is the Hilbert sum of the subspaces $K_i = H_1 \otimes e_i$ canonically isomorphic to H_1.

Let $T \in \mathscr{L}(H_1)$; we will show that the operator $S = T \otimes 1$ in H is represented by the following matrix $(S_{i,j})$:

$$\begin{cases} \text{si } i \neq j & S_{i,j} = 0 \\ \text{si } i = j & S_{i,j}(x \otimes e_i) = Tx \otimes e_i. \end{cases}$$

Indeed, let R be the operator in H having the indicated matrix; to show that $S = R$ it suffices to see that

$$S(x \otimes y) = R(x \otimes y) \qquad \forall x \in H_1,\ y \in H_2;$$

now

$$S(x \otimes y) = Tx \otimes y$$

by definition and

$$R(x \otimes y) = R(x \otimes \sum_i y_i e_i) = \sum_i y_i R(x \otimes e_i)$$

$$= \sum_i y_i (Tx \otimes e_i) = Tx \otimes y.$$

The mapping $T \to T \otimes 1$ is an injective homomorphism of $\mathscr{L}(H_1)$ into $\mathscr{L}(H)$ called *ampliation*; if we identify each space K_i to H_1 we can say that S is a diagonal matrix whose diagonal elements are equal to T and that the ampliation consists of repeating the same operator a certain number of times.

§ 2. *Fundamental properties of ∗-algebras*

1. *Definitions*

In the sequel we will call *∗-algebra* any self-adjoint (i.e. which contains the adjoints of its elements) subalgebra of $\mathscr{L}(H)$ which contains 1.

Examples. $\mathscr{L}(H)$, C_H (set of scalar operators).

If A is a ∗-algebra, the set of operators commuting with every element of A is another ∗-algebra, called the *commutant* of A and denoted by A'; the center of A is $A \cap A'$; A is commutative if and only if $A \subset A'$.

Examples. We have $\mathscr{L}(H)' = C_H$ and $C'_H = \mathscr{L}(H)$.

The *bicommutant* $A'' = (A')'$ of A obviously contains A.

Let A be a $*$-algebra and M an arbitrary set of vectors; we denote by X^A_M the subspace generated by the vectors Tx for $T \in A$ and $x \in M$, i.e. the set of linear combinations $T_1x_1 + \ldots + T_px_p$; X^A_M is invariant under every operator of A, hence the corresponding projection operator, denoted by P^A_M, belongs to A'. If in particular M is reduced to a single vector x, X^A_x is the set of Tx where $T \in A$; any projection operator of the form P^A_x is said to be *cyclic*; x is said to be *totalizing* if $X^A_x = H$.

2. *Study of the bicommutant*

Proposition 1.1. For every $*$-algebra we have $A'' = A$.

We first show the following: for every $S \in A''$ and every $x \in H$ there exists a $T \in A$ such that $Tx = Sx$; indeed, P^A_x commutes with S, hence X^A_x is invariant under S; X^A_x contains x (because A contains 1) and hence also Sx, whence our assertion.

To prove the proposition we must show that, if we take a basis $(e_1, \ldots, e_n)$ of H and an operator $S \in A''$ there exists a $T \in A$ such that

$$Te_1 = Se_1, \ldots Te_n = Se_n.$$

Let $K = H \oplus \ldots \oplus H$, n times, and let $z = (e_1, \ldots, e_n)$; for all $T \in \mathcal{L}(H)$, let $\tilde{T}$ be the operator represented by the diagonal matrix $\tilde{T}_{i,i} = T$; the $\tilde{T}$ for $T \in A$ form a $*$-algebra $\tilde{A}$ isomorphic to A.

We show that $\tilde{S} \in (\tilde{A})''$; first if $R \in (\tilde{A})'$, R has a matrix $(R_{i,j})$ and, for all $T \in A$,

$$\sum_k R_{i,k}\tilde{T}_{k,j} = \sum_k \tilde{T}_{i,k}R_{k,j}$$

$$R_{i,j}T = TR_{i,j}$$

hence $R_{i,j} \in A'$; then R commutes with S: indeed

$$R_{i,j}S = SR_{i,j}$$

that is to say

$$\sum_k R_{i,k}S_{k,j} = \sum_k S_{i,k}R_{k,j}.$$

According to the beginning of the proof, there exists a $\tilde{T} \in \tilde{A}$ (hence a $T \in A$) such that

$$\tilde{T}z = \tilde{S}z$$

That is to say

$$(Te_1, \ldots Te_n) = (Se_1, \ldots Se_n).$$

Corollary 1.1. If $A' = C_H$, $A = \mathscr{L}(H)$.

Corollary 1.2. Center A = center $A' = A \cap A'$.

Remarks. – We have a decreasing bijective correspondence $A \leftrightarrow A'$.
– If $T \in A$, the decomposition $T = T_1 + iT_2$ is done in A.

Proposition 1.2. Let T be a hermitian element of A; every spectral projection operator and, if $T \geqq 0$, its square root $T^{\frac{1}{2}}$ belong to A.

Indeed, these operators belong ot A''.

Corollary 1.3. A is the $*$-algebra generated by its projection operators.

Corollary 1.4. If the only invariant subspaces under every element of A are $\{0\}$ and H, we have $A = \mathscr{L}(H)$.

Which is expressed by saying that every *irreducible* $*$-algebra is identical to $\mathscr{L}(H)$.

Corollary 1.5. Every $T \in A$ is a linear combination of unitary operators of A.

We can suppose T is hermitian and $\|T\| \leqq 1$; then $1 - T^2 \geqq 0$; set

$$U = T + i(1 - T^2)^{\frac{1}{2}};$$

we readily see that U is unitary and that $T = \frac{1}{2}(U + U^*)$.

3. *Induced algebras*

Let A be a $*$-algebra and E a subspace of H such that $P_E \in A'$; the mapping $T \in A \to T_E$ is a $*$-algebra homomorphism. i.e.

$$(T + S)_E = T_E + S_E$$

$$(TS)_E = T_E S_E$$

$$(T^*)_E = (T_E)^*.$$

For $T \in A$ the T_E form a $*$-algebra in E denoted by A_E and called the *induced algebra*; the mapping $T \to T_E$ is called an *induction*.

Proposition 1.3. The commutant $(A_E)'$ of A_E is the set of the S_E where $S \in A'$ and $SP_E = P_E S = S$ (i.e. S leaves E invariant and is zero in $H \ominus E$).

If S is of this form we immediately see that S_E commutes with every T_E. Conversely, let R be an operator in E which commutes with the T_E; define S in H by

$$Sx = \begin{cases} Rx \text{ if } x \in E \\ 0 \quad \text{if } x \in H \ominus E. \end{cases}$$

We have $S \in A'$; indeed, let $T \in A$; to show that $ST = TS$ it suffices to see that $STx = TSx$

a) for $x \in E$: then $STx = RT_E x = T_E Rx = TSx$

b) for $x \in H \ominus E$: then $STx = 0 = TSx$. Q. E. D.

Let us consider also $H \ominus E$ and $A_{H \ominus E}$; when T runs over A, T_E and $T_{H \ominus E}$ run over A_E and $A_{H \ominus E}$ respectively, in general not independently (they can even be completely connected, cf. Lemma 1.2); saying that they run over them independently amounts to saying that A is the *product* of A_E and $A_{H \ominus E}$.

Proposition 1.4. A is the product of A_E and $A_{H \ominus E}$ if and only if P_E belongs to the center of A.

Suppose $P_E \in A \cap A'$; let $R \in A_E$ and $S \in A_{H \ominus E}$; there exist T_1 and $T_2 \in A$ such that $(T_1)_E = R$ and $(T_2)_{H \ominus E} = S$; set

$$T = T_1 P_E + T_2 P_{H \ominus E};$$

we have $T \in A$, $T_E = T_1$ and $T_{H \ominus E} = T_2$.

Conversely, suppose A is the product; there exists a $T \in A$ such that $T_E = 1$ and $T_{H \ominus E} = 0$; then $T = P_E$.

Remark. This is part of the theory of reduction (cf. § 3); we can say that A is decomposable as a product if and only if its center does not reduce to C_H - - - whence the interest of studying $*$-algebras whose center reduces to C_H.

Definition. We call a *factor* any $*$-algebra whose center reduces to C_H.

4. *Isomorphisms of $*$-algebras*

We have already spoken about homorphisms of $*$-algebras; the concept of isomorphism is hence clear; we mention that such an isomorphism is norm-preserving.

Examples: *spatial* isomorphisms. Suppose we have two Hilbert spaces H and H' and an isomorphism U of H onto H' (isomorphism means here the conservation of scalar products); the mapping $T \to UTU^{-1}$ is an isomorphism of $\mathcal{L}(H)$ onto $\mathcal{L}(H')$ which consists of "carrying" T under U; if T describes a given $*$-algebra A in H, UTU^{-1} describes *a* $*$-algebra B in H' and we have an isomorphism of A onto B; such an isomorphism is said to be *spatial*.

Examples of non-spatial isomorphisms: the ampliations; an induction can be an isomorphism without being spatial (cf. Lemma 1.2).

Proposition 1.5. Let H and H' be two Hilbert spaces; every isomorphism of $\mathcal{L}(H)$ onto $\mathcal{L}(H')$ is spatial.

Let Φ be such an isomorphism, $e_1, \ldots, e_n$ an orthonormal basis of H; for $i = 1, \ldots, n$ we define an operator V_i in H by

$$V_i(e_1) = e_i, \quad V_i(e_2) = \cdots = V_i(e_n) = 0;$$

we get

$$V_i^*(e_j) = \begin{cases} e_1 \text{ if } j = i \\ 0 \text{ otherwise} \end{cases}$$

and

$$V_j^* V_i = \begin{cases} P_{e_1} \text{ if } i = j \\ 0 \text{ otherwise.} \end{cases}$$

P_{e_1} is a minimal projection operator into $\mathcal{L}(H)$ hence $\Phi(P_{e_1})$ is one into $\mathcal{L}(H')$; it is hence the projection operator onto a certain normed vector f_1; set

$$f_i = \Phi(V_i)f_1 \quad \text{for} \quad i = 2, \ldots n:$$

the f_i are orthonormed:

$$(f_i \mid f_j) = (\Phi(V_i)f_1 \mid \Phi(V_j)f_1) = (\Phi(V_j^* V_i)f_1 \mid f_1)$$
$$= \begin{cases} (\Phi(P_{e_1})f_1 \mid f_1) = 1 \text{ if } i = j \\ 0 \qquad\qquad\qquad \text{otherwise;} \end{cases}$$

the f_i form a basis of H', for otherwise there would exist a projection operator Q orthogonal to the P_{f_i} and (since $P_{f_i} = \Phi(P_{e_i})$) $\Phi^{-1}(Q)$ would be a projection operator orthogonal to the P_{e_i}, which is impossible.

We define an isomorphism U of H onto H' by $Ue_i = f_i$ and an isomorphism Ψ of $\mathcal{L}(H)$ onto $\mathcal{L}(H')$ by $\Psi(T) = UTU^{-1}$; we will show that

$\Psi = \Phi$; since the V_i^* generate the $*$-algebra $\mathscr{L}(H)$, it suffices to see that

$$\Psi(V_i^*) = \Phi(V_i^*) \qquad \forall i$$

or

$$\Psi(V_i^*)f_j = \Phi(V_i^*)f_j \qquad \forall i, j;$$

now

$$\text{first member} = UV_i^*U^{-1}f_j = UV_i^*e_j = \begin{cases} f_1 \text{ if } i = j \\ 0 \text{ otherwise} \end{cases}$$

$$\text{second member} = \Phi(V_i^*V_j)f_1 = \begin{cases} f_1 \text{ if } i = j \\ 0 \text{ otherwise.} \end{cases}$$

§ 3. *The theory of reduction*

1. *Decomposable operators and diagonalizable operators*

Consider a space H which is a Hilbert sum $H = \bigoplus_{i=1}^{r} H_i$. An operator T in H is said to be *decomposable* if its matrix $(T_{i,j})$ is diagonal, i.e. if $T_{i,j} = 0$ for $i \neq j$; we then write T_i instead of $T_{i,i}$ and we have

$$(Tx)_i = T_i x_i.$$

In particular, if all the T_i are scalars, T is said to be *diagonalizable*; if $T_i = \lambda_i \cdot 1$ we get

$$(Tx)_i = \lambda_i x_i$$

and T consists of multiplying each component x_i of x by λ_i; we also say that T is the operator of *multiplication* by the function $i \to \lambda_i$.

The diagonalizable (resp. decomposable) operators form a $*$-algebra Z (resp. Z_1); Z is commutative and isomorphic to the algebra of the complex functions defined on the set $\{1, 2, \ldots, r\}$, i.e. to $\mathfrak{C}^r$; finally it is obvious that every operator of Z commutes with every operator of Z_1, in other words that $Z_1 \subset Z'$ and $Z \subset Z_1'$.

Proposition 1.6. The $*$-algebras Z and Z_1 are commutants of each other.

Show that $Z' \subset Z_1$, which will imply the proposition (we note in passing that this assertion is well-known for ordinary matrices: every matrix which commutes with all the diagonal matrices is itself diagonal); let

$$S = (S_{i,j}) \in Z'$$

and let

$$T = (T_{i,j}) \in Z \quad \text{where} \quad T_{i,j} = \begin{cases} 0 & \text{if } i \neq j \\ \lambda_i \cdot 1 & \text{if } i = j. \end{cases}$$

We have $TS = ST$, hence

$$\lambda_i S_{i,j} = S_{i,j} \lambda_j \quad \forall i,j;$$

since the λ_i are arbitrary, this implies that $S_{i,j} = 0$ for $i \neq j$, i.e. $S \in Z_1$. Q. E. D.

Henceforth we will write Z' instead of Z_1.

2. *Decomposable $*$-algebras*

Take a $*$-algebra A_i in each H_i; the set of decomposable T such that $T_i \in A_i \ \forall i$ is a $*$-algebra which we denote

$$\sum_{i=1}^{r} {}^{\oplus} A_i;$$

abstractly (i.e. making abstraction of the spaces H_i and H on which act the A_i and $\sum^{\oplus} A_i$) $\sum^{\oplus} A_i$ is the *product* of the A_i; a $*$-algebra of this type is said to be *decomposable.*

Examples. $Z = \sum^{\oplus} C_{H_i}$, $Z' = \sum^{\oplus} \mathcal{L}(H_i)$.

Properties. $$(\sum^{\oplus} A_i)' = \sum^{\oplus} A_j';$$

if A is decomposable we obviously have $Z \subset A \subset Z'$; more precisely:

Proposition 1.7. *A $*$-algebra A in H is decomposable if and only if $Z \subset A \subset Z'$.*

The sufficiency of this condition remains to be proved; each $T \in A$ is decomposable, say $T = (T_i)$; let A_i be the $*$-algebra in H_i composed of the T_i (for fixed i and T running over A); we obviously have $A \subset \sum^{\oplus} A_i$ and we will show that $A \supset \sum^{\oplus} A_i$; it suffices to show that

$$A' \subset (\sum^{\oplus} A_i)' = \sum^{\oplus} A_i'.$$

We note that $Z \subset A' \subset Z'$; hence if $S \in A'$, S is decomposable, say $S = (S_i)$; since S commutes with all the $T \in A$, S_i commutes with all the T_i, i.e. $S_i \in A_i'$ and $S \in \sum^{\oplus} A_i'$.

Remarks.

– This proposition is a generalization of Proposition 1.4.

– If $A \subset Z'$, the *elements* of A are decomposable, but A is not necessarily; their components do not necessarily vary independently.

The P_{H_i} are *the* minimal projection operators of Z; more generally, the projection operators of Z correspond biunivocally to the functions $i \to \lambda_i$, with $\lambda_i = 0$ or 1, that is to say to the subsets of $\{1, 2, \ldots, r\}$.

3. *The structure of commutative $*$-algebras*

Proposition 1.8. Any commutative $*$-algebra in a space H is the algebra of the diagonalizable operators for a decomposition $H = \bigoplus_{i=1}^{r} H_i$ and this decomposition is unique.

Let Y be a commutative $*$-algebra; consider the minimal projection operators of Y; they are orthogonal two by two (indeed, if P and Q are two such projection operators, since they commute $PQ = QP$ is a projection operator of A strictly less than P and Q; hence zero); there is hence a finite number of them, say $P_1, \ldots, P_r$; we have

$$P_1 + P_2 + \cdots P_r = 1$$

because otherwise $1 - P_1 - \ldots P_r$ would majorize another minimal projection operator; hence if $H_1, \ldots, H_r$ are the corresponding subspaces, we have decomposed H into a Hilbert sum $H_1 \oplus \ldots \oplus H_r$. Let Z be the algebra of the operators which are diagonalizable for this decomposition; Y and Z have the same minimal projection operators; if we can show that a commutative $*$-algebra is generated by its minimal projection operators, the proposition will be proved; now, a $*$-algebra is generated by its projectors; it suffices hence to show that every projection operator is the sum of minimal projection operators – – – the proof is identical to that in the beginning, in the case $P = 1$.

Uniqueness: the H_i are the subspaces corresponding to the minimal projection operators of Y.

Corollary 1.6. Every commutative $*$-algebra is isomorphic to an algebra $\mathfrak{C}^r$.

Remarks.

– Making the decomposition of Proposition 1.8. is also called *diagonalizing* Y.

– One can verify without trouble that the following conditions are equivalent:

(i) Y is a maximal commutative $*$-algebra;

(ii) $Y = Y'$;
(iii) Y admits a totalizing vector;
(iv) the H_i have dimension 1.

4. *The structure of arbitrary $*$-algebras*

Proposition 1.9. Any $*$-algebra A in a space H is of form $\sum_{i=1}^{r}{}^{\oplus} A_i$, where the A_i are factors, for a certain decomposition of H into Hilbert sums.

The center Z of A is the algebra of the operators which are diagonalizable for a certain decomposition $H = \bigoplus_{i=1}^{r} H_i$; since $Z \subset A \subset Z'$, A is decomposable, say $A = \sum{}^{\oplus} A_i$; we know that $Z = \text{center } A = \sum{}^{\oplus}$ center A_i; hence center $A_i = C_{H_i}$ and the A_i are factors.

Corollary 1.7. Every $*$-algebra is isomorphic to a product of algebras of the form $\mathscr{L}(H)$.

That follows from corollary 1.8.

§ 4. *The structure of factors*

Examples of factors: C_H, $\mathscr{L}(H)$, $\mathscr{L}(H_1) \otimes C_{H_2}$; we will see that all factors are of this last type.

Lemma 1.1. Let A be a factor; if $P_E \in A$ and $P_E \neq 0$, then $X_E^A = H$.

We know that $P_E^A \in A'$; we also have $P_E^A \in A$: X_E^A is indeed invariant under any $R \in A'$, since

$$R \sum_i S_i x_i = \sum_i S_i R x_i \qquad (x_i \in E,\ S_i \in A)$$

and $Rx_i \in E$; since $P_E^A \neq 0$, we have $P_E^A = 1$.

Lemma 1.2. Let A be a factor; if $P_E \in A'$, the induction $T \to T_E$ is an isomorphism of A onto A_E (we obviously suppose $P_E \neq 0$).

Suppose $T \in A$ and $T_E = 0$; we have $TP_E = 0$, hence for all $S \in A'$

$$STP_E = TSP_E = 0$$

which means that T is zero on $X_E^{A'}$, hence zero.

Lemma 1.3. Let A be a $*$-algebra: if P_E is a minimal projection operator of A', we have $A_E = \mathscr{L}(E)$.

It suffices to show that the only projection operators of A'_E are 0 and 1; now (Proposition 1.3) any projection operator of A'_E is of form S_E where S is a projection operator of A' majorized by P_E, hence equal to 0 or to P_E.

Proposition 1.10. Every factor is spatially isomorphic to a factor of form $\mathscr{L}(H_1) \otimes C_{H_2}$.

Let $P_{E_1}, \ldots, P_{E_r}$ be minimal projection operators of A', orthogonal two by two and with sum equal to 1; we have $A_{E_i} = \mathscr{L}(E_i)$; the induction $T \to T_{E_i}$ is an isomorphism $\wedge_i$ of A onto $\mathscr{L}(E_i)$; let Φ_i be the isomorphism $\wedge_i \circ \wedge_i^{-1}$ of $\mathscr{L}(E_1)$ onto $\mathscr{L}(E_i)$; from Proposition 1.5, there exists an isomorphism U_i of E_1 onto E_i such that

$$\Phi_i(T) = U_i T U_i^{-1} \qquad \forall T \in \mathscr{L}(E_1);$$

hence we have

$$S_{E_i} = U_i S_{E_1} U_i^{-1} \qquad \forall S \in A.$$

Set $H_1 = E_1$, $H_2 =$ space of dimension r, with basis $\{e_1, \ldots, e_r\}$; $H_1 \otimes H_2$ is the Hilbert sum of the subspaces $H_1 \otimes e_i$; define an isomorphism V of $H_1 \otimes H_2$ onto H by the condition that V sends $H_1 \otimes e_i$ onto E_i under

$$V(x \otimes e_i) = U_i x.$$

We will show that the mapping $T \to V^{-1}TV$ is a spatial isomorphism of A onto $\mathscr{L}(H_1) \otimes C_{H_2}$; it is a spatial isomorphism of A onto a certain $*$-algebra in $H_1 \otimes H_2$; let $T \in A$; I say that

$$V^{-1}TV = T_{E_1} \otimes 1;$$

first $V^{-1}TV$ leaves invariant each subspace $H_1 \otimes e_i$ since T leaves each subspace E_i invariant; it remains to show that $V^{-1}TV$ and $T_{E_1} \otimes 1$ act in the same manner in each $H_1 \otimes e_i$; to do this we take $x \in H_1$ and we must verify that

$$(V^{-1}TV)(x \otimes e_i) = (T_{E_1} \otimes 1)(x \otimes e_i);$$

Now we have

$$\begin{aligned} \text{first member} &= V^{-1}TU_i x = V^{-1}T_{E_i}U_i x = V^{-1}U_i T_{E_1} x \\ &= T_{E_1} x \otimes e_i = \text{second member}. \end{aligned}$$

So we do indeed have

$$V^{-1}TV = T_{E_1} \otimes 1 \in \mathscr{L}(H_1) \otimes C_{H_2};$$

finally T_{E_1} obviously runs over the entire $\mathscr{L}(H_1)$.

Corollary 1.8. Every factor is isomorphic to an algebra $\mathscr{L}(H)$.

Remarks

– One can show, with the notations of the previous proposition, that

$$A' = C_{H_1} \otimes \mathscr{L}(H_2);$$

if we represent the elements of $H_1 \otimes H_2$ by quantities with two indices, we can say that the operators of A act on the first index and those of A' act on the second.

– $\mathscr{L}(H_1 \otimes H_2)$ is isomorphic to the tensor product of two algebras isomorphic respectively to A and to A'; this explains the term "factor".

– The $*$-algebras are semi-simple algebras and among them the simple algebras are the factors.

§ 5. *Traces*

Definition. A *trace* on a $*$-algebra A is a linear form φ, which is positive (i.e. $\varphi(T) \geqq 0$ if $T \geqq 0$) and such that $\varphi(UTU^{-1}) = \varphi(T)$ for every unitary operator $U \in A$. It is *faithful* if $T \geqq 0$ and $\varphi(T) = 0$ imply that $T = 0$.

Proposition 1.11. Every trace is a central linear form, i.e.

$$\varphi(ST) = \varphi(TS) \qquad \forall S, T \in A.$$

This is true for unitary S, then for arbitrary S (Corollary 1.5).

Example. The usual trace on $\mathscr{L}(H)$. Let $\{e_1, \ldots, e_n\}$ be an orthogonal basis of H; set

$$\varphi(T) = \sum_i (Te_i \mid e_i);$$

φ is obviously a linear form; it is positive and faithful because if $T \geqq 0$

$$\varphi(T) = \sum_i \|T^{\frac{1}{2}}e_i\|^2$$

and $\varphi(T) = 0 \Rightarrow T^{\frac{1}{2}} = 0 \Rightarrow T = 0$.

For all T we have $\varphi(T^*T) = \varphi(TT^*)$; indeed,

$$\varphi(T^*T) = \sum_i \| Te_i \|^2$$

$$\varphi(TT^*) = \sum_i \| T^*e_i \|^2 = \sum_i \sum_j |(T^*e_i \mid e_j)|^2$$

$$= \sum_j \sum_i |(e_i \mid Te_j)|^2 = \sum_j \| Te_j \|^2.$$

We prove that $\varphi(UTU^{-1}) = \varphi(T)$: suppose first that $T \geqq 0$; then

$$\varphi(UTU^{-1}) = \varphi(UT^{\frac{1}{2}} \cdot (UT^{\frac{1}{2}})^*) = \varphi((UT^{\frac{1}{2}})^* UT^{\frac{1}{2}})$$

$$= \varphi(T^{\frac{1}{2}} U^{-1} U T^{\frac{1}{2}}) = \varphi(T);$$

if now T is arbitrary, T is a linear combination of positive operators and the relation is still true.

The form φ is hence a faithful trace; it is independent of the chosen orthonormed basis because if $\{f_1, \ldots, f_n\}$ is another one, there exists an operator U such that $f_i = Ue_i$ and

$$\sum_i (Tf_i \mid f_i) = \sum_i (TUe_i \mid Ue_i) = \sum_i (U^{-1}TUe_i \mid e_i) = \varphi(T).$$

Proposition 1.12. Two traces on a factor are proportional.

We can suppose $A = \mathscr{L}(H)$ and show that any trace φ is proportional to the usual trace; φ assumes the same value α on all the projection operators of dimension 1 since we go from one to another by means of a unitary operator; φ assumes the value $m\alpha$ on any projection operator of dimension m since such a projection operator is the sum of m projection operator of dimension 1; hence φ and the usual trace are proportional on any projection operator, hence on any operator, as the linear combination of projection operators.

CHAPTER II

GENERALITIES ON VON NEUMANN ALGEBRAS

§ 1. *Preliminaries*

1. *Vectors, subspaces, operators*

We will denote by H a complex Hilbert space, that is to say the vector space composed of the families $x = (x_i)_{i \in I}$ (where I is an arbitrary set) of complex numbers satisfying

$$\sum_{i \in I} |x_i|^2 < +\infty$$

and endowed with the *scalar product*

$$(x \mid y) = \sum_{i \in I} x_i \bar{y}_i;$$

any vector x admits a *norm* $\|x\| = (x \mid x)^{\frac{1}{2}}$.

We consider on H the *strong topology* ($x \to 0$ if $\|x\| \to 0$) and the *weak topology* ($x \to 0$ if $(x \mid y) \to 0$ for all y).

All that was said in Chapter I, § 1, n°. 1 remains valid with the following modifications:

a) we only speak about *closed* vector subspaces (it is not necessary to specify for which topology);

b) the concept of Hilbert sum extends to an arbitrary family $(X_j)_{j \in J}$ of subspaces; $\bigoplus_{j \in J} X_j$ is then the set of vectors $\sum_j x_j$ ($x_j \in X_j$) such that $\sum_j \|x_j\|^2 < +\infty$;

c) we only speak about *continuous* linear operators (same remark as in *a*));

d) an operator T is said to be *unitary* if it preserves the scalar product and is *surjective*;

e) all the orthonormal bases of H have the same power, called the *Hilbert dimension* of H.

We call the *support* of an operator T the complementary set of the kernel of T and *image* of T the closure of $T(H)$. We will use the ordering relation $T \geqq S \Longleftrightarrow T - S \geqq 0$ on the set of positive operators; any majorized right-filtering set admits an upper bound. The algebra $\mathscr{L}(H)$ is *complete* for the norm $\|T\|$.

Remark. We call any complete normed $*$-algebra satifying the axioms (i) to (v) a *C^*-algebra*; it is clear that any subalgebra of $\mathscr{L}(H)$, which is self-adjoint and closed for the norm topology is a C^*-algebra; one can prove that any C^*-algebra is conversely isomorphic to a closed self-adjoint subalgebra of an algebra $\mathscr{L}(H)$; later we will use the theory of commutative C^*-algebra.

2. *Projection operators. Partially isometric operators.*

All that was said in Chapter I, § 1, no. 2, remains valid. We will also use the concept of *partially isometric operator*, written briefly p. i. o. (which was actually already used in the proof of Proposition 1.5.); an operator V is said to be partially isometric if it sends isometrically a subspace E onto a subspace F and is zero in $H \ominus E$; then V^* sends F isometrically onto E and is zero on $H \ominus F$; the restrictions of V and V^* to E and F are inverse mappings; we have $V^*V = P_E$, $VV^* = P_F$; P_E and P_F are called the *initial and final* projection operators of V.

3. *Decomposition theorems*

a) and b) remain true without changes.

c) *Polar decomposition.* Any operator T can be *uniquely* written in the form $T = V\,|T|$ where $|T| = (T^*T)^{\frac{1}{2}}$ and where V is a p. i. o. whose support is the support of T and whose image is the image of T; we recall that the support of T is also the support and the image of $|T|$.

d) For the spectral decomposition we retain the following: let T be a hermitian operator; the *spectrum* of T is the compact and non-empty set of real numbers such that $T - \lambda 1$ admits no inverse in

$\mathcal{L}(H)$; with each real λ we can associate a projection operator E_λ in such a way that the mapping $\lambda \to E_\lambda$ is increasing and that, for $x, y \in H$, we have

$$(Tx \mid y) = \int_{-\infty}^{+\infty} \lambda \cdot d(E_\lambda x \mid y)$$

in the Stieltjes sense; with each interval $[a, b]$ we associate the projection operator $E_b - E_a$, then with each Borel set we associate a projection operator by the Lebesgue process; the projection operators obtained in this way are called the *spectral projection operators* of T; they commute with any operator which commutes with T; we have

$$TE_0 \leqq 0 \leqq T(1 - E_0);$$

if T is positive and non-zero there exists a $\lambda > 0$ such that

$$T \geqq \lambda(1 - E_\lambda) \neq 0.$$

Finally T is the limit for the norm topology of linear combinations of spectral projection operators.

4. *Operators in a Hilbert sum.*

What was said in Chapter I remains true and extends to an arbitrary family of subspaces H_i; the matrices $(T_{i,j})$ are then infinite and the formula for the product converges in a sense which we will not specify.

5. *Operators in a tensor product.*

We will merely add the following: the *Hilbert* tensor product $H_1 \otimes H_2$ is the completed Hilbert space of the algebraic tensor product.

6. *Topologies on* $\mathcal{L}(H)$

We will use two topologies, besides the topology deduced from the norm:

a) The *strong topology*: it is the topology of strong simple convergence, i.e. $T \to 0$ if $\|Tx\| \to 0$ for all x; to obtain an arbitrary neighbourhood of 0 we take $x_1, \ldots, x_p \in H$ and the set of T satisfying

$$\|Tx_1\| \leqq 1, \ldots \|Tx_p\| \leqq 1.$$

This topology is compatible with the vector space structure of $\mathscr{L}(H)$ (i.e. the mappings $(S, T) \to S + T$ and $(\lambda, T) \to \lambda T$ are continuous), but not with its $*$-algebra structure; in particular the mapping $(S, T) \to ST$ is not in general continuous; it is continuous if S belongs to the unit ball of $\mathscr{L}(H)$, which we denote by $\mathscr{L}_1(H)$; it is always separately continuous.

If H has countable basis, $\mathscr{L}_1(H)$ is a *Polish* space (i.e. metrizable, complete and with countable basis).

b) The *weak topology*: it is the topology of weak simple convergence, i.e. $T \to 0$ if $(Tx \mid y) \to 0$ $\forall x$ and y; to obtain an arbitrary neighbourhood of 0 we take $x_1, \ldots, x_p, y_1, \ldots, y_p \in H$ and the set of T satisfying

$$|(Tx_1 \mid y_1)| \leqq 1, \ldots |(Tx_p \mid y_p)| \leqq 1.$$

This topology is compatible with the vector space structure of $\mathscr{L}(H)$, but not with its $*$-algebra structure; $\mathscr{L}_1(H)$ is *compact* and, if H has countable basis, metrizable and with countable basis.

§ 2. *Definitions and fundamental properties of von Neumann algebras*

1. *$*$-algebras of operators*

We call here a $*$-algebra of operators in a Hilbert space H any self-adjoint subalgebra of $\mathscr{L}(H)$ which contains 1. Examples: $\mathscr{L}(H)$, C_H (the set of scalar operators).

The definitions and properties given in Chapter I remain valid with the following modification: X_M^A is the set of limits (strong or weak) of linear combinations

$$T_1x_1 + \cdots + T_px_p \qquad (T_1 \cdots T_p \in A,\ x_1 \ldots x_p \in M)$$

and X_x^A is the set of limits of vectors Tx $(T \in A)$.

2. *Study of the bicommutant*

Lemma 2.1. Every $*$-algebra A is strongly dense in its bicommutant A''.

We will first prove the following: for all $S \in A''$ and all $x \in H$, there exists a $T \in A$ such that $\|Tx - Sx\| \leqq 1$; P_x^A belongs to A', hence it commutes with S, hence X_x^A remains invariant under S; X_x^A contains x, hence also Sx which is hence the strong limit of vectors Tx with $T \in A$.

In order to prove the lemma we must prove that for any $S \in A''$ and $x_1, \ldots, x_p \in H$ there exists a $T \in A$ such that

$$\| Tx_i - Sx_i \| \leqq 1 \quad \text{for} \quad i = 1, \ldots, p$$

let $K = H \oplus \ldots HSp$ times, and $z = (x_1, \ldots, x_p)$; for all $T \in \mathcal{L}(H)$, let $\tilde{T}$ be the operator with diagonal matrix $\tilde{T}_{i,i} = T$; the $\tilde{T}$ $(T \in A)$ form a $*$-algebra $\tilde{A}$ and $\tilde{S} \in \tilde{A}''$ (cf. proof of Proposition 1.1); there exists hence a $T \in A$ such that $\|\tilde{T}z - \tilde{S}z\| \leqq 1$ and T satisfies the required conditions.

Proposition 2.1. The following conditions are equivalent for a $*$-algebra A:

(i) $A = A''$;

(ii) A is weakly closed;

(iii) A is strongly closed;

(i) $\Rightarrow$ (ii) since the commutant of a $*$-algebra is always weakly closed;

(ii) $\Rightarrow$ (iii) is obvious;

(iii) $\Rightarrow$ (i) from the lemma.

Definition. A von Neumann algebra is a $*$-algebra satisfying the above three conditions.

Corollary 2.1. If A is a von Neumann algebra such that $A' = C_H$ we have $A = \mathcal{L}(H)$.

Corollary 2.2. If A is a von Neumann algebra we have center A = center $A' = A \cap A'$.

The remarks following Corollary 1.2. remain valid for von Neumann algebras.

Proposition 2.2. Let T be a hermitian element of a von Neumann algebra A; every spectral projection operator and, if $T \geqq 0$, its square root $T^{\frac{1}{2}}$ belong to A.

Indeed, these operators belong to A''.

Corollary 2.3. A is the von Neumann algebra generated by its projection operators.

Indeed, every hermitian operator is the limit in norm of linear combinations of spectral projection operators.

Corollary 2.4. If the only subspaces which remain invariant under A are $\{0\}$ and H, we have $A = \mathscr{L}(H)$.

Remark. A $*$-algebra B with this property is sometimes called *irreducible*; this does not imply that $B = \mathscr{L}(H)$, but only that B is strongly dense in $\mathscr{L}(H)$, and is even equivalent to it.

Corollary 2.5. Any element of A is a combination of unitary elements of A.

Same proof as for Corollary 1.5.

Corollary 2.6. If T belongs to A and if $T = V\,|T|$ is its polar decomposition, V and $|T|$ belong to A.

We already know that $|T| \in A$; for V, it suffices to see that V commutes with any unitary operator of A', say U; now

$$T = UTU^{-1} = UVU^{-1}U|T|U^{-1} = UVU^{-1}|T|$$

and UVU^{-1} is obviously partially isometric; since the polar decomposition is unique, $UVU^{-1} = V$.

3. *Induced algebras*

The exposition of Chapter I remains valid for von Neumann algebras; in particular we have:

Proposition 2.3. If A is a von Neumann algebra and if $P_E \in A'$, the commutant $(A_E)'$ of A_E is the set of S_E where $S \in A'$ and $SP_E = P_ES = S$.

Proposition 2.4. A is the product of A_E and $A_{H\ominus E}$ if and only if $P_E \in A \cap A'$.

Definition. A von Neumann algebra whose centre is reduced to C_H is called a *factor*.

4. *Isomorphism of von Neumann algebras*

The exposition of Chapter I remains valid for von Neumann algebras; in particular we have:

Proposition 2.5. If H and H' are two Hilbert spaces, every isomorphism of $\mathscr{L}(H)$ onto $\mathscr{L}(H')$ is spatial.

The proof of this is very similar to that of Proposition 1.5.

CHAPTER III

THE THEORY OF REDUCTION

All that was said in Chapter I, § 3, remains true, but becomes definitely insufficient, even when we take infinite Hilbert sums; because the application of the results of this section to the study of $*$-algebras was based on the existence of minimal projection operators, an existence which does not occur in general. We are thus lead to replacing the concept of Hilbert sum by another, more general – – – that of Hilbert integral.

In this chapter we will only consider topological or Hilbert spaces *with countable bases,* though some results will be valid without this restriction.

§ 1. *Definition of measurable fields of Hilbert spaces*

Let Z be a locally compact topological space with countable basis and μ a positive measure on Z; to each $z \in Z$ we associate a Hilbert space $H(z)$: we obtain a *field of Hilbert spaces*; a *field of vectors* x consists of giving for each z a vector $x(z) \in H(z)$, i.e. an element of the product space $\prod H(z)$; to define a structure of *measurable field* on the field of Hilbert spaces, we must say which will be the measurable vector fields; to do this we take a sequence (x_i) of vector fields such that

a) the functions $z \to (x_i(z) \mid x_j(z))$ are measurable;

b) for all z the vectors $x_i(z)$ form a total sequence in $H(z)$.

Such a sequence x_i is called a *fundamental family* of measurable vector fields. Then a vector field x will be said to be *measurable* if all the functions

$$z \to (x(z) \mid x_i(z))$$

are measurable; the measurables vector fields form a vector space; we show that if x and y are measurable fields, the functions $z \to (x(z) \mid y(z))$ is measurable; we first show that $\|x(z)\|$ is measurable; for all finite sequences $\varrho = (\varrho_i)$ of complex rational numbers we set $x_\varrho = \sum \varrho_i x_i$; for all z the vectors $x_\varrho(z)$ are everywhere dense in $H(z)$, hence

$$\|x(z)\| = \sup\left(|(x(z) \mid x_\varrho(z))| \,/\, \|x_\varrho(z)\|\right)$$

where the second member is taken to be equal to 0 when $x_\varrho(z) = 0$; $|x(z)|$ is measurable as the upper bound of a countable family of measurable functions. Finally $(x(z) \mid y(z))$ is measurable by virtue of the identity

$$4(x \mid y) = (x + y \mid x + y) - (x - y \mid x - y)$$
$$+ i(x + iy \mid x + iy) - i(x - iy \mid x - iy).$$

By the Schmidt orthonormalization process we construct a *measurable field of orthonormal bases*, i.e. a sequence $y_1, y_2, \ldots$ of measurable vector fields such that

– if $\dim H(z)$ is infinite, $y_1(z), y_2(z), \ldots$ form an orthonormal basis of $H(z)$

– if $\dim H(z) = d < +\infty$, $y_1(z), \ldots, y_d(z)$ form an orthonormal basis of $H(z)$ and the others are zero.

(The construction, too lenghty to be described in detail, can be found in [1].)

In the sequel we will identify two measurable fields which are equal almost everywhere; the set of measurable fields satisfying $\int \|x(z)\|^2 \, d\mu < +\infty$ is a Hilbert space for the scalar product

$$(x \mid y) = \int (x(z) \mid y(z)) \, d\mu \, .$$

(This assertion is an easy generalization of the Fischer-Riesz theorem stating that the space $L^2(Z, \mu)$ is a Hilbert space; cf. example 2.)

It is called the *Hilbert integral* of the field $z \to H(z)$ and we denote it by $H = \overset{\oplus}{\int} H(z) \, d\mu$.

Example 1. If μ is atomic, every vector field is measurable so we find again the concept of Hilbert sum; in this case the $H(z)$ are subspaces of H, which is not true in general.

Example 2. If all the $H(z)$ have dimension 1 we can choose the fundamental family so that the measurable vector fields are the measurable complex functions; then H is merely $L^2(Z, \mu)$.

Example 3. Denote by K a fixed Hilbert space and take the *constant field* $z \to K$; we can choose the fundamental family in such a way that the measurable vector fields are the measurable mappings (for the strong or weak topology) of Z in K; the Hilbert integral is then the space of the square integrable mappings of Z into K, space which we denote by $L^2_K(Z, \mu)$; we specify that this space is canonically isomorphic to $L^2(Z, \mu) \otimes K$ and that we define an isomorphism Φ of the second onto the first by setting

$$\Phi\left(\sum_{i=1}^{n} f_i \otimes \xi_i\right) = \sum_{i=1}^{n} f_i \xi_i$$

$$(f_i \in L^2(Z, \mu),\ \ \xi_i \in K,\ f_i\xi_i = \text{the mapping } z \to f_i(z)\xi_i).$$

Lemma 3.1. Let (x_i) be a fundamental family of square integrable vector fields; the set of fields $f(z)\, x_i(z)$ where $f \in \mathfrak{K}(Z)$ is total in H.

($\mathfrak{K}(Z)$ denotes the set of continuous functions with compact support on Z.)

Because if x is orthogonal to all these fields we have

$$\int f(z)\ (x_i(z) \mid x(z))\ \mathrm{d}\mu = 0 \qquad \forall f \in \mathcal{K}(Z)$$

and hence for all i: $(x_i(z) \mid x(z)) = 0$ except on a negligeable set N_i; $\cup N_i$ is negligeable and on $Z - \cup N_i$ we have $(x_i(z) \mid x(z)) = 0$ for all i, hence $x(z) = 0$; finally $x = 0$.

Remarks

– The lemma remains valid if we only take f's which are everywhere dense in $\mathfrak{K}(Z)$; it follows that H has *countable basis*.

– In fact any measurable field of Hilbert spaces, at least if dim $H(z)$ is constant, is equivalent in a certain sense to a constant field; more precisely, let K be a Hilbert space of the same dimension as the $H(z)$; we take a measurable field of orthonormal bases $(e_i(z))$, an orthonormal basis (g_i) of K, and to the field $z \to e_i(z)$ we associate the field $z \to g_i$.

§ 2. *Decomposable operators*

A *field of operators* consists of giving, for each z, an operator $T(z) \in \mathcal{L}(H(Z))$; such a field is said to be *measurable* if the functions $z \to (T(z)\, x_i(z) \mid x_j(z))$ are measurable. Then if x is a measurable field, the field $T(z)\, x(z)$ is measurable: to see this we must show that, for all i, $(T(z)\, x(z) \mid x_i(z))$ is measurable; now this is equal to $(x(z) \mid T(z)^*\, x_i(z))$ and it suffices to verify that the field $T(z)^*\, x_j(z)$ is measurable; i.e. that for all j, $(T(z)^*\, x_i(z) \mid x_j(z))$ is measurable; now this is equal to $(x_i(z) \mid T(z)\, x_j(z))$.

Suppose now that $\|T(z)\|$ is essentially bounded and let λ be its essential upper bound; let $x = (x(z)) \in H$; the field $T(z)\, x(z)$ is measurable and we have almost everywhere

$$\|T(z)\, x(z)\| \leqq \lambda\, \|x(z)\|$$

whence

$$\int \|T(z)\, x(z)\|^2 \, \mathrm{d}\mu \leqq \lambda^2 \int \|x(z)\|^2 \, \mathrm{d}\mu;$$

in other words if we denote by Tx the field $z \to T(z)\, x(z)$, we have $Tx \in H$ and $\|Tx\| \leqq \lambda\|x\|$; T is a continuous linear operator on H, with norm $\leqq \lambda$, denoted by $\int^{\oplus} T(z)\, \mathrm{d}\mu$; we will say that any operator in H obtained in this way is *decomposable*.

Proposition 3.1. We have $\|T\| = \lambda$.

Let $x = (x(z)) \in H$ and $f \in \mathfrak{K}(Z)$; we have

$$\begin{aligned} \int |f(z)|^2\, \|T(z)\, x(z)\|^2 \, \mathrm{d}\mu &= \int \|T(z)\, f(z)\, x(z)\|^2 \, \mathrm{d}\mu \\ &= \|Tfx\|^2 \leqq \|T\|^2\, \|fx\|^2 \\ &= \|T\|^2 \int |f(z)|^2\, \|x(z)\|^2 \, \mathrm{d}\mu \\ &= \int |f(z)|^2\, \|T\|^2\, \|x(z)\|^2 \, \mathrm{d}\mu \end{aligned}$$

whence, since f is arbitrary,

$$\|T(z)\, x(z)\| \leqq \|T\|\, \|x(z)\|;$$

now taking x_i which form an everywhere dense sequence in each $H(z)$ we obtain almost everywhere

$$\|T(z)\, x_i(z)\| \leqq \|T\|\, \|x_i(z)\| \qquad \forall i$$

hence,

$$\|T(z)\| \leqq \|T\|.$$

almost everywhere.

Example. Consider a constant field $z \to K$; one proves that the measurable fields of operators are the strongly measurable mappings $Z \to \mathscr{L}(K)$; in particular we have the constant fields of operators $z \to T$; then the integral operator, carried over into $L^2(Z, \mu) \otimes K$, is $1 \otimes T$.

Immediate properties

– $\int^{\oplus} (S(z) + T(z))\, d\mu = \int^{\oplus} S(z)\, d\mu + \int^{\oplus} T(z)\, d\mu$

– $\int^{\oplus} \lambda T(z)\, d\mu = \lambda \int^{\oplus} T(z)\, d\mu$

– $\int^{\oplus} (S(z)T(z))\, d\mu = \int^{\oplus} S(z)\, d\mu \cdot \int^{\oplus} T(z)\, d\mu$

– $\int^{\oplus} T(z)^*\, d\mu = \left(\int^{\oplus} T(z)\, d\mu\right)^*$

– A decomposable operator admits a unique decomposition up to the negligeable sets.

– The decomposable operators form a $*$-algebra B; we will see later that B is a von Neumann algebra.

Lemma 3.2. There exists a sequence of decomposable operators $\int^{\oplus} T_i(z)\, d\mu$ such that for all z, $\mathscr{L}(H(z))$ is the von Neumann algebra generated by the $T_i(z)$.

Using the second remark following Lemma 3.1, we are first reduced to a constant field $z \to K$; it suffices then to take constant fields $T_i(z) = S_i$ where the S_i generate $\mathscr{L}(K)$.

Remark. We mention in passing a flaw in the theory; when we have a von Neumann algebra A in H all of whose elements are decomposable, we cannot in general associate to each $T \in A$ a decomposition $T = \int^{\oplus} T(z)\, d\mu$ such that for almost all z the mapping $T \to T(z)$ is a $*$-algebra homomorphism of A into $\mathscr{L}(H(z))$; this is due, among others, to the non-compatibility of the strong and weak topologies with the $*$-algebra structure of $\mathscr{L}(H)$ (chapter II, § 1, no. 6); it can however be done for every $*$-algebra with countable basis for the norm topology and it must be mentioned here that the von Neumann algebras *do not have countable basis* for the norm topology – – – except of course the finite-dimensional ones.

§ 3. *Diagonalizable operators*

Let $f \in L^\infty(Z, \mu)$ (the space of essentially bounded measurable functions); the field of operators $z \to f(z) \cdot 1$ is measurable and has essentially bounded norm; we can hence consider the integral operators, which we will denote by T_f; we have

$$\|T_f\| = \|f\|_\infty;$$

$f \to T_f$ is an isomorphism of the normed $*$-algebra $L^\infty(Z, \mu)$ (a commutative C^*-algebra) onto a $*$-algebra of operators D which is hence a commutative C^*-algebra; it is moreover immediate that this isomorphism is bicontinuous when we endow $L^\infty(Z, \mu)$ with its weak topology of dual of $L^1(Z, \mu)$ and D with the weak topology. The operators T_f are often called "multiplication operators".

Lemma 3.3. We have $B = D'$.

Obviously $B \subset D'$; let us prove that $D' \subset B$; let $T \in D'$; take the x_ϱ we had in the biginning of § 1 but supposing here that the x_i are square integrable; set

$$Tx_i = y_i = (y_i(z))$$

$$y_\varrho = \sum \varrho_i y_i = Tx_\varrho;$$

for all $f \in \mathfrak{K}(Z)$ we have

$$T_f y_\varrho = T_f T x_\varrho = T T_f x_\varrho$$

$$\|T_f y_\varrho\|^2 \leqq \|T\|^2 \, \|T_f x_\varrho\|^2$$

$$\int |f(z)|^2 \, \|y_\varrho(z)\|^2 \, d\mu \leqq \|T\|^2 \int |f(z)|^2 \, \|x_\varrho(z)\|^2 \, d\mu$$

$$\|y_\varrho(z)\| \leqq \|T\| \, \|x_\varrho(z)\|$$

almost everywhere say for $z \in Z - N$ with N negligeable; for all $z \in Z - N$ there exists a continuous linear operator $T(z)$ in $H(z)$ such that

$$T(z)\, x_\varrho(z) = y_\varrho(z) \qquad \forall \varrho$$

and we get $\|T(z)\| \leqq \|T\|$; in particular $T(z)\, x_i(z) = y_i(z)$; for $z \in N$ set $T(z) = 0$; we will show that $T' = \int^\oplus T(z)\, d\mu$ is equal to T; first $T'x_i = y_i = Tx_i$; then if $f \in \mathfrak{K}(Z)$

$$T'fx_i = T'T_f x_i = T_f T' x_i = T_f T x_i = T T_f x_i = T f x_i$$

and from Lemma 3.1, we get $T' = T$.

Lemma 3.4. We have $D = B'$.

First $D \subset B'$ and also $D \subset B$ whence $B' \subset D' = B$; we show that $B' \subset D$; let $T \in B'$; T is decomposable, say $T = \int^{\oplus} T(z)\, d\mu$; let $T_i = \int^{\oplus} T_i(z)\, d\mu$ be a sequence with the properties of Lemma 3.2; since T commutes with the T_i, $T(z)$ commutes almost everywhere with all the $T_i(z)$, hence it is scalar and T is diagonalizable.

We have thus proved the

Theorem 3.1. The set of diagonalizable operators is a commutative von Neumann algebra D; the mapping $f \to T_f$ is an isomorphism of normed $*$-algebras of $\mathscr{L}^\infty(Z, \mu)$ onto D as well as a homeomorphism for the weak topologies; the commutant D' of D is the algebra of the decomposable operators.

§ 4. *Decomposable von Neumann algebras*

A field of von Neumann algebras consists of giving for all z a von Neumann algebra $A(z)$ in $H(z)$; it is said to be *measurable* if we can find measurable fields $T_1(z), T_2(z), \ldots$ such that for all z the $T_i(z)$ generate $A(z)$.

Examples. $\mathscr{L}(H(z))$, by the Lemma 3.2; $C_{H(z)}$.

Lemma 3.5. If the field $A(z)$ is measurable, the field $A(z)'$ is measurable also.

We can reduce ourselves to a constant field $z \to K$; we then have strongly measurable mappings $z \to T_i(z)$ of Z into $\mathscr{L}(K)$ such that for all z the $T_i(z)$ generate $A(z)$; we can obviously suppose that $\|T_i(z)\| \leq 1$; then restricting ourselves if needs be to compact subsets of Z; we can suppose that the mappings $z \to T_i(z)$ are strongly continuous.

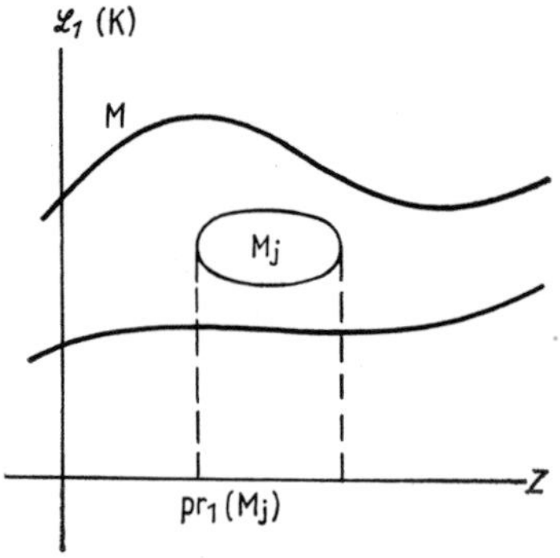

Let M be the subset of $Z \times \mathscr{L}_1(K)$ composed of the pairs (z, S) such that $S \in A(z)'$, i.e. $ST_i(z) = T_i(z)\, S$ for all i; M is closed in $Z \times \mathscr{L}_1(K)$ which is Polish; its topology has hence a countable base

$M_1, M_2, \ldots$; the M_j are Borel in $Z \times \mathscr{L}_1(K)$ and their projections $pr_1(M_j)$ are analytic; there exists then (von Neumann theorem using the measurability of the analytic sets) a measurable section of M_j, that is to say a measurable mapping $z \to S_j(z)$ of $\mathrm{pr}_1(M_j)$ into $\mathscr{L}_1(K)$ such that we have $(z, S_j(z)) \in M_j$ for all z; we extend $S_j(z)$ by 0 outside $pr_1(M_j)$ and we obtain thus measurable fields $z \to S_j(z)$; it is clear that $S_j(z) \in A(z)'$; finally the $S_j(z)$ generate $A(z)'$: indeed, let $S \in A(z)'$; (z, S) belongs to M and has a fundamental system of neighbourhoods $M_{n_1}, M_{n_2}, \ldots$; $(z, S_{n_p}(z))$ tends to (z, S) hence $S_{n_p}(z)$ tends strongly to S.

Lemma 3.6. The set A of decomposable operators $T = \int^{\oplus} T(z)\, \mathrm{d}\mu$ such that $T(z) \in A(z)$ almost everywhere is a von Neumann algebra.

Let $(S_j(z))$ be a sequence of essentially bounded measurable fields such that for all z the $S_j(z)$ generate $A(z)'$ and let $S_j = \int^{\oplus} S_j(z)\, \mathrm{d}\mu$; we have $S_j \in A'$. On the other hand $D \subset A \subset D'$ and hence $D \subset A'' \subset D'$; we will show that $A'' \subset A$; let $T \in A''$, $T = \int^{\oplus} T(z)\, \mathrm{d}\mu$; T commutes with the S_j, hence $T(z)$ commutes almost everywhere with all the $S_j(z)$ i.e. $T(z) \in A(z)'' = A(z)$ and $T \in A$. Q. E. D.

We denote by $\int^{\oplus} A(z)\, \mathrm{d}\mu$ the von Neumann algebra of the lemma and we will say that any von Neumann algebra obtained in this way is *decomposable*; we then readily obtain the relation

$$\left(\int^{\oplus} A(z)\, \mathrm{d}\mu\right)' = \int^{\oplus} A(z)'\, \mathrm{d}\mu$$

as well as the uniqueness of the decomposition, up to the negligeable sets.

Examples

– $D = \int^{\oplus} C_{H(z)} \mathrm{d}\mu$, $D' = \int^{\oplus} \mathscr{L}(H(z))\, \mathrm{d}\mu$.

– Consider a constant field $z \to K$; any constant field $z \to A$ is measurable and the integral algebra, carried over into $L^2(Z, \mu) \otimes K$, is $D_0 \otimes A$ ($D_0 =$ the algebra of the operators which are diagonalizable in $L^2(Z, \mu)$), that is to say, the von Neumann algebra generated by the finite sums $\sum_n T_n \otimes S_n$ where $T_n \in D_0$ and $S_n \in A$.

Theorem 3.2. A von Neumann algebra A is decomposable if and only if we have $D \subset A \subset D'$.

The condition is necessary: cf. proof of Lemma 3.6.

The condition is sufficient: if $D \subset A \subset D'$ we also have $D \subset A' \subset D'$; let $T_1, T_2, \ldots$ and S_1 S_2 $\ldots$ be sequences of operators generating A and A' respectively with $T_i = \int^{\oplus} T_i(z)\, d\mu$, $S_j = \int^{\oplus} S_j(z)\, d\mu$; for all z, let $A(z)$ be the von Neumann algebra generated by the $T_i(z)$; we will show that $A = \int^{\oplus} A(z)\, d\mu$. We first note that almost everywhere the $T_i(z)$ commute with the $S_j(z)$ and consequently all the elements of $A(z)$ commute with the $S_j(z)$.

We have $\int^{\oplus} A(z)\, d\mu \subset A$: indeed, if $T \in \int^{\oplus} A(z)\, d\mu$, $T(z)$ commutes with the $S_j(z)$ almost everywhere, T commutes with the S_j and $T \in A$. To show that $A \subset \int^{\oplus} A(z)\, d\mu$ let us show that $\int^{\oplus} A(z)'\, d\mu \subset A'$: if $R \in \int^{\oplus} A(z)'\, d\mu$, $R(z)$ commutes with the $T_i(z)$ almost everywhere, R commutes with the T_i and $R \in A'$.

Proposition 3.2. Let $A = \int^{\oplus} A(z)\, d\mu$ be a decomposable von Neumann algebra; the $A(z)$ are almost all factors if and only if D is the center A.

(Note that in any case the center of A contains D.)

The field $z \to A(z) \cap A(z)'$ is measurable: to see this it suffices to see that the field $z \to (A(z) \cap A(z)')'$ is measurable; now $(A(z) \cap A(z)')'$ is the von Neumann algebra generated by $A(z)$ and $A(z)'$ and the assertion follows immediately form the definition and the Lemma 3.5. Moreover $A \cap A' = \int^{\oplus} (A(z) \cap A(z)')\, d\mu$; then saying that $A \cap A' = D$ amounts to saying that $A \cap A' = \int^{\oplus} C_{H(z)} d\mu$, hence that $A(z) \cap A(z)' = C_{H(z)}$ almost everywhere.

§ 5. *The structure of commutative von Neumann algebras*

We recall some results of the Gelfand theory concerning commutative C^*-algebras. (See Commutative Banach Algebras § 7.3).

Examples: if X is a non-compact locally compact space the algebra $C_0(X)$ of the continuous functions tending to 0 at infinity is a commutative C^*-algebra without unit; if X is a compact space, the algebra

$\mathfrak{C}(X)$ of the continuous functions is a commutative C^*-algebra with unit. One shows that all commutative C^*-algebras are of one of the above types.

[First suppose A has a unit; any non-zero homomorphism of A into the field of complex numbers is called a *character*; every character is automatically continuous and has norm ≤ 1; the set X of the characters is contained in the unit ball of the dual space A' and it is easy to see that it is compact for the weak topology; to each $a \in A$ we associate the continuous function on X: $\hat{a}(x) = x(a)$; we obtain a homomorphism of A into $\mathfrak{C}(X)$ and all the difficulty of the theory resides in proving that it is an isometric isomorphism. X is called the *spectrum* of A.

Suppose now that A has no unit; we can adjoin a unit to A by replacing it by the set $\tilde{A}$ of the pairs (a, k) where $a \in A$ and $k \in \mathfrak{C}$ the product being defined by

$$(a, k)\,(a', k') = (aa' + ka' + k'a,\, kk')$$

let x_0 be the character of $\tilde{A}$: $(a, k) \to k$; the *spectrum* of A is merely $X - \{x_0\}$ and A identifies with the set of continuous functions on X which are zero at x_0 that is to say with the set of continuous functions on $X - \{x_0\}$ which are zero at infinity.]

We add that A has countable basis if and only if X has countable basis.

Applying this to commutative von Neumann algebras we get the

Proposition 3.3. Every commutative von Neumann algebra is isomorphic to the algebra of the continuous functions on a compact space.

Remark. The spectra of commutative von Neumann algebras present certain particularities: they do not in general have countable basis (cf. remark in § 2); on the other hand they are *Stonian* spaces and are in particular *totally discontinuous*; this is due among others, to the fact that any von Neumann algebra contains a "large number" of projection operators.

We will now give a "spatial" description of an arbitrary commutative von Neumann algebra D by showing that it is the algebra of the diagonalizable operators for a certain decomposition of H into Hilbert integrals; to do this we could use the spectrum of D a method which has the advantage of leading to *continuous* fields of Hilbert spaces; in fact we will avoid this method because of the unpleasant nature of this spectrum and we will use the spectrum of a C^*-algebra with countable basis for the norm topology and which is strongly dense in D (such an algebra is obtained by taking a sequence $T_1, T_2, \ldots$ generating the von Neumann algebra D and the C^*-algebra generated by this sequence); let thus D_0 be such an algebra containing 1 and let Z be its spectrum; the notation $a \to \hat{a}$ will be replaced here by $F \to f$; we immediately note that since D_0 is not unique, Z will not be intrinsic.

Theorem 3.3. The algebra D is spatially isomorphic to the algebra of the operators which are diagonalizable for a certain Hilbert integral on Z.

Particular case: suppose first that D admits a totalizing vector x. We define a positive measure μ on Z by setting $\mu(f) = (Fx \mid x)$ for all $f \in \mathfrak{C}(Z)$. We will construct an isomorphism of H onto $L^2(Z, \mu)$; to do this we associate the function 1 to x and, more generally, the function f to each element Fx; we get

$$(Fx \mid F_1x) = (F_1^*Fx \mid x) = \mu(\bar{f}_1 f) = (f \mid f_1);$$

in other words our correspondence $Fx \to f$ preserves scalar products; it extends thus to an isomorphism Φ of H onto a closed subspace of $L^2(Z, \mu)$, which contains $\mathfrak{C}(Z)$, and is hence equal to $L^2(Z\ \mu)$. It remains to be seen that Φ transforms D into the algebra of the diagonalizable operators (or operators of multiplication by the functions of $L^\infty(Z, \mu)$; if first $G \in D_0$, we get

$$\Phi G \Phi^{-1} = T_g$$

because

$$\Phi G \Phi^{-1} f = \Phi G \cdot Fx = \Phi \cdot GFx = gf = T_g f;$$

hence Φ transforms D_0 into the algebra of the operators T_g $(g \in \mathfrak{C}(z))$; on the other hand μ has support Z (readily verified) and $\mathfrak{C}(Z)$ identifies with a subalgebra of $L^\infty(Z, \mu)$, which is everywhere dense for the weak topology; hence Φ transforms D into the algebra of the diagonalizable operators (cf. Theorem 3.1.).

General case. According to Zorn we can find vectors $x_1, x_2, \ldots$ and subspaces $H_1, H_2, \ldots$ such that

$$H_n = X_{x_n}^D \quad \text{and} \quad H = \bigoplus H_n;$$

we define positive measures μ_n on Z by $\mu_n(f) = (Fx_n \mid x_n)$; the problem is to "stack up" properly the spaces $L^2(Z, \mu_n)$ on Z.

We denote by μ the measure $\sum_n \mu_n/2^n$ (or any other measure such that the μ_n have basis μ); the theorem of Radon-Nikodym gives functions Ψ_n such that $\mu_n = \Psi_n\mu$; let Z_n be the μ-measurable set of the z where $\Psi_n \neq 0$; let Z'_p ($p = 0, 1, \ldots, \infty$) be the μ-measurable set of the z which belong to exactly p sets Z_n. On the other hand let K_∞ be an infinitedimensional Hilbert space and K_p the subspace generated by $e_1, \ldots, e_p$ ($e_1, e_2, \ldots$ orthonormal basis of K), $K_0 = \{0\}$. For the field $z \to H(z)$ we take a field which is constant on each Z'_p equal then to K_p.

We are going to construct an isomorphism Φ of H onto $\int^{\oplus} H(z)\, d\mu$; to do this we associate to x_n the field y_n defined by

$$y_n(z) = \begin{cases} 0 & \text{if } z \notin Z_n \\ (\Psi_n(z))^{\frac{1}{2}} e_p & \text{if } z \text{ belongs to } Z_n \text{ and to exactly } p-1 \\ & \text{predecessors;} \end{cases}$$

we have $\|y_n(z)\| = (\Psi_n(z))^{\frac{1}{2}}$ for all z; we then associate the field fy_n to Fx_n; we get

$$(Fx_n \mid F_1x_n) = \int \bar{f}_1 f(z)\, d\mu_n = \int \bar{f}_1 f(z)\, \Psi_n(z)\, d\mu$$

$$= \int \bar{f}_1 f(z)\, \|y_n(z)\|^2\, d\mu$$

$$= \int (fy_n \mid f_1 y_n)\, d\mu = (fy_n \mid f_1 y_n);$$

consequently our correspondence $Fx_n \to fy_n$ extends into an isomorphism Φ_n of H_n onto a closed subspace of $\int^{\oplus} H(z)\, d\mu$; the images of the H_n are orthogonal two by two: let be Fx_n and Gx_m with $n < m$; $f(z)\, y_n(z)$ and $g(z)\, y_m(z)$ can be non-orthogonal only if z belongs to Z_n and to exactly $p-1$ predecessors and also to Z_m and to exactly $p-1$ predecessors - - - which obviously never happens. The images of the H_n generate $\int^{\oplus} H(z)\, d\mu$: it suffices to see that for all $p = 1, 2, \ldots, \infty$ $\Phi(H)$ contains the fields $z \to e_1, \ldots, z \to e_p$ over Z'_p; now if $z \in Z'_p$, z belongs to a set of form $Z_{n_1} \cap \ldots \cap Z_{n_p}$ with $n_1 < n_2 < \ldots < n_p$ and

$$y_{n_1}(z) = (\Psi_{n_1}(z))^{\frac{1}{2}} e_1, \ldots, y_{n_p}(z) = (\Psi_{n_p}(z))^{\frac{1}{2}} e_p.$$

So we see that Φ is indeed an isomorphism of H onto $\int^{\oplus} H(z)\, d\mu$; there remains to see that it does indeed transform D into the algebra of the diagonalizable operators – – – which is done as in the particular case we examined earlier.

Corollary 3.1. *A* von Neumann algebra which is commutative in a Hilbert space with countable basis is isomorphic to an algebra $L^\infty(Z, \mu)$ where Z has countable basis.

Remark. Obtaining the decomposition of Theorem 3.3 is sometimes called "diagonalizing" D.

Study of the uniqueness

– Intrinsic structure (i.e. making abstraction of H and of its decomposition). First, if μ and μ' are equivalent, $L^\infty(Z, \mu)$ and $L^\infty(Z, \mu')$ are isomorphic; then if we have Z and μ, Z' and μ' and a bijection φ of Z less a negligeable set onto Z' less a negligeable set transforming μ into μ', $L^\infty(Z, \mu)$ and $L^\infty(Z', \mu')$ are isomorphic; it can be proved (von Neumann) that we obtain, by combining these two transformations, all the $L^\infty(Z', \mu')$ which are isomorphic to a given $L^\infty(Z, \mu)$. It was also proved (D. Maharam) that $L^\infty(Z, \mu)$ and $L^\infty(Z', \mu')$ are isomorphic if μ and μ' have atomic parts with the same number of masses and diffuse parts which are simultaneously zero or non-zero; this is why we can always take $Z = [0, 1]$ and μ = Lebesgue measure plus possibly some point masses.

– Spatial structure. The result is a long one to state; roughly we will say that if two fields $H(z)$ and $H'(z')$ over (Z, μ) and (Z', μ') give rise to spatially isomorphic algebras of diagonalizable operators, we get a bijection φ as above and isomorphisms $V(z)$ of $H(z)$ onto $H'(\varphi(z))$.

Remark. It can readily be verified, as in Chapter I, that the following conditions are equivalent:

(i) D is maximal commutative;

(ii) $D = D'$;

(iii) D admits a totalizing vector;

(iv) the H(z) of the decomposition associated with D are almost all one-dimensional.

Relation to spectral theory

Let T be a hermitian operator; let D be the (commutative) von Neumann algebra generated by T, $H = \int^{\oplus} H(z)\, d\mu$ a decomposition of H

associated with D; T is the operator of multiplication by a certain real function f; the spectrum of T is the set of real λ such that $\mu(f^{-1}(V)) > 0$ for all neighbourhoods V of λ; because saying that this is so amounts to saying that the function $1/(f(z) - \lambda)$ is not essentially bounded. Let ν be the measure on $\mathfrak{R}$, image of μ under f, i.e., by definition, $\nu(\varphi) = \mu(\varphi \circ f)$; its support is the spectrum of T; we can also carry over under f the operator measure $g \to T_g$:

$$\varphi \in L^\infty(\mathfrak{R}, \nu) \to \text{operator } T_{\varphi \circ f};$$

then for any real λ the projection operator E_λ of the classical theory is merely the projection operator of D associated with $f^{-1}\,(]-\infty, \lambda[)$; more generally, the spectral projection operators of T are exactly the projection operators of D. We can also, of course, carry out the decomposition of H over $\mathfrak{R}$ and ν. Finally T is said to have *simple spectrum* if D is maximal commutative.

§ 6. *The structure of arbitrary von Neumann algebras*

Theorem 3.4. Every von Neumann algebra in a Hilbert space with countable basis is spatially isomorphic to an algebra $\int^{\oplus} A(z)\, \mathrm{d}\mu$ where the $A(z)$ are factors.

It suffices (Proposition 3.2) to diagonalize the center of the given algebra.

The decomposition we obtain is called the "central decomposition of the algebra".

CHAPTER IV

STUDY OF THE STRUCTURE OF FACTORS

§ 1. *Traces on a von Neumann algebra*

Definition. A *trace* on a Neumann algebra A is a function φ defined on the set A^+ of the positive elements of A, with finite or non-finite positive real values, and satisfying:

(i) φ is additive and $\varphi(kT) = \begin{cases} 0 \text{ if } k = 0 \\ k\varphi(T) \text{ if } k > 0; \end{cases}$

(ii) $\varphi(UTU^{-1}) = \varphi(T)$ for any unitary operator $U \in A$;

(iii) for any majorized right-filtering family $T_i \in A^+$ we have

$$\varphi(\sup T_i) = \sup \varphi(T_i).$$

A trace φ is said to be

- *finite* if it only assumes finite values;
- *semi-finite* if $\forall T \in A^+$, $\exists S \in A^+$, $S \neq 0$, $S \leqq T$, $\varphi(S) < +\infty$;
- *faithful* if $T \in A^+$, $\varphi(T) = 0 \Rightarrow T = 0$.

Remark. Condition (iii) indicates a certain continuity; with regard to this we recall that $\sup T_i$ is strongly adherent to the set of the T_i.

Lemma 4.1. Any bilateral ideal I of A is self-adjoint; any element of I is a linear combination of positive elements of I.

a) Let $T \in I$; let $T = V\,|T|$ be its polar decomposition; we have V and $|T| \in A$ (cf. Corollary 2.6); then

$$T^* = |T|V^* = V^*V|T|V^* = V^*TV^* \in I.$$

b) Let also $T \in I$; we can suppose it is hermitian; from Chapter I, § 1, no. 3,d, T admits spectral projection operators E and F such that

$$E + F = 1,\ TE \geqq 0,\ TF \leqq 0;$$

we have E and $F \in A$ (Proposition 2.2) and $T = TE - T(-F)$.

Lemma 4. Let φ be a trace on A and $\mathfrak{m}_0$ the set of $T \in A^+$ such that $\varphi(T) < +\infty$;

(i) the set $\mathfrak{n}$ of the $T \in A$ such that $T^*T \in \mathfrak{m}_0$ is a bilateral ideal;

(ii) set $\mathfrak{m} = \mathfrak{n}^2$ (the bilateral ideal composed of the finite sums $\sum T_i S_i$ where T_i and $S_i \in \mathfrak{n}$); $\mathfrak{m}_0$ is the set of positive elements of $\mathfrak{m}$.

Proof of (i): if S and $T \in \mathfrak{n}$, we have

$$(S+T)^*(S+T) = S^*S + T^*T + S^*T + T^*S$$

$$0 \leqq (S-T)^*(S-T) = S^*S + T^*T - S^*T - T^*S$$

hence

$$S^*T + T^*S \leqq S^*S + T^*T$$

$$(S+T)^*(S+T) \leqq 2S^*S + 2T^*T$$

$$S + T \in \mathfrak{n}.$$

To see that $T \in \mathfrak{n}$, $S \in A \Rightarrow ST$ and $TS \in \mathfrak{n}$ it suffices to see that it is true for unitary S (cf. Corollary 2.5); then

$$(ST)^*(ST) = T^*S^*ST = T^*T \in \mathfrak{m}_0$$

$$(TS)^*(TS) = S^*T^*TS \in \mathfrak{m}_0.$$

Proof of (ii): first $\mathfrak{m}_0 \subset \mathfrak{m}^+$: if $T \in \mathfrak{m}_0$ we have $T = T^{\frac{1}{2}} T^{\frac{1}{2}}$ and $T^{\frac{1}{2}} \in \mathfrak{n}$, $T \in \mathfrak{m}$; then $\mathfrak{m}^+ \subset \mathfrak{m}_0$: let $T \in \mathfrak{m}^+$; $T = \sum R_j S_j^*$ where R_j and $S_j \in \mathfrak{n}$; the identity

$$4RS^* = (R+S)(R+S)^* - (R-S)(R-S)^* + i(R+iS)(R+iS)^* - i(R-iS)(R-iS)^* \quad (1)$$

and the fact that T is hermitian imply that

$$4T = \sum [(R_j + S_j)(R_j + S_j)^* - (R_j - S_j)(R_j - S_j)^*]$$

$$\leqq \sum [(R_j + S_j)(R_j + S_j)^*]$$

$$T \in \mathfrak{m}_o.$$

Proposition 4.1. There exists a unique linear form $\dot{\varphi}$ on $\mathfrak{m}$ which coincides with φ on $\mathfrak{m}_0$; we have $\dot{\varphi}(ST) = \dot{\varphi}(TS)$ in the two following cases:

(i) $S \in A$ and $T \in \mathfrak{m}$

(ii) A and $T \in \mathfrak{n}$.

The beginning is obvious; then (i) is obvious if S is unitary and $T \in \mathfrak{m}_0$, then if A is unitary and $T \in \mathfrak{m}$, by linearity; finally for arbitrary S. Proof of (ii): it amounts to proving that $\dot{\varphi}(ST^*) = \dot{\varphi}(T^*S)$; it reduces to the case $S = T$ by using the identity (i); then if $T = V\,|T|$ is the polar decomposition of T we have

$$TT^* = V|T|^2V^*$$

$$T^*T = |T|V^*VT = |T|^2 = V^*V|T|^2$$

the assertion follows from (i) since $V\,|T|^2 \in \mathfrak{m}$. Q. E. D.

We now suppose φ is *semi-finite* and *faithful*; for S and $T \in \mathfrak{n}$ we set

$$(S \mid T) = \mathring{\varphi}(ST^*).$$

Proposition 4.2. $(S \mid T)$ is a scalar product for which $\mathfrak{n}$ is a separable prehilbert space; we also have the following properties:

(i) $(S \mid T) = (T^* \mid S^*)\ \forall S, T \in \mathfrak{n}$;
(ii) $(RS \mid T) = (S \mid R^*T)\ \forall R, S, T \in \mathfrak{n}$:
(iii) the mapping $T \to ST$ is continuous;
(iv) the elements ST are everywhere dense in $\mathfrak{n}$.

The beginning and the properties (i) and (ii) are immediate; property (iii): we have

$$T^*S^*ST \leqq \|S\|^2T^*T$$

hence

$$(ST \mid ST) = \mathring{\varphi}(STT^*S^*) = \mathring{\varphi}(T^*S^*ST) \leqq \|S\|^2\,(T \mid T);$$

we will *assume* property (iv).

A $*$-algebra with the above-mentioned properties is called a *Hilbert algebra.* Let K be the completed Hilbert space of $\mathfrak{n}$; the operators (in $\mathfrak{n}$) U_R and V_R ($R \in \mathfrak{n}$) defined by

$$U_RS = RS \quad \text{and} \quad V_RS = SR$$

are continuous and extend into continuous operators in K also denoted by U_R and V_R; every U_R and every V_R commute; hence the von Neumann algebras $\mathcal{U}$ and $\mathcal{V}$ generated by the U_R and the V_R, respectively, commute; more precisely, we have the following fundamental result which we will assume (commutation theorem): $\mathcal{U}$ and $\mathcal{V}$ are commutants of one another.

§ 2. *Classification of factors*

Theorem 4.1. Two faithful semi-finite traces on a factor are proportional.

Sketch of the proof. Let φ_1 and φ_2 be two such traces; replacing, for instance φ_2 by $\varphi_1 + \varphi_2$ the question reduces to showing that the theorem holds in the case where $\varphi_1(T) \leqq \varphi_2(T)$ for all $T \in A^+$; then $\mathfrak{n}_1 \supset \mathfrak{n}_2$; on the other hand one extends the definition of U_R and V_R to the case where $R \in A$ and one shows that the mappings $R \to U_R$ and $R \to V_R$ are respectively an isomorphism and an antiisomorphism of A onto $\mathcal{U}$ and $\mathcal{V}$; $\mathcal{U}$ and $\mathcal{V}$ are hence factors. The scalar product $\dot{\varphi}_1(ST^*)$ on $\mathfrak{n}_2$ is continuous and can be written

$$\mathring{\varphi}_1(ST^*) = \mathring{\varphi}_2(M(S)\, T^*)$$

where M is a continuous operator in the completed Hilbert space of $\mathfrak{n}_2$; one verifies that M commutes with $\mathcal{U}$ and $\mathcal{V}$; M is then a scalar k and $\varphi_1 = k\varphi_2$.

Remark. Traces are the object of a theory, called theory of "non-commutative integration", similar in many ways to the usual theory of integration.

Definitions

A factor is said to be *of type I* or *discrete* if it is isomorphic to the algebra $\mathcal{L}(H)$ for a certain space H, and more precisely

- of type I_n if H has finite dimension n
- of type I_∞ if H has infinite dimension

A non-discrete factor is said to be *continuous* and more precisely

- of type II_1 if it admits a faithful finite trace
- of type II_∞ if it admits a non-finite semi-finite faithful trace
- of type III if it admits no semi-finite faithful trace.

The types I_n and II_1 are also called *finite types*.

§ 3. *Discrete factors*

Theorem 4.2. The following properties are equivalent for a factor A;

(i) A is discrete;

(ii) A contains a minimal projection operator;

(iii) A' is discrete;

(iv) A' contains a minimal projection operator;

Clearly it suffices to prove (*i*) $\Rightarrow$ (ii) and (ii) $\Rightarrow$ (iii); the first implication is obvious; for the second: let P_E be a minimal projection operator of A; we show, as in Lemmas 1.2 and 1.3, that the induction of A' onto A'_E is an isomorphism and that $A'_E = \mathscr{L}(E)$.

Theorem 4.3. A discrete factor is spatially isomorphic to a factor of form $\mathscr{L}(H_1) \otimes C_{H_2}$.

The proof is in all ways analogous to that of Proposition 1.10.

Study of the trace on factors of type I_∞

Take $A = \mathscr{L}(H)$ and let (e_i) be an orthonormal basis of H; for all $T \geqq 0$ we set

$$\varphi(T) = \sum_i (Te_i \mid e_i);$$

the axiom (i) of traces is trivially verified; to prove axiom (ii) we first show that

$$\varphi(T^*T) = \varphi(TT^*) \qquad \forall T \in \mathscr{L}(H);$$

we have

$$\varphi(T^*T) = \sum_i (T^*Te_i \mid e_i) = \sum_i \|Te_i\|^2$$

$$\varphi(TT^*) = \sum_i (TT^*e_i \mid e_i) = \sum_i \|T^*e_i\|^2$$

$$= \sum_i \sum_j |(T^*e_i \mid e_j)|^2 = \sum_j \sum_i |(e_i \mid Te_j)|^2$$

$$= \sum \|Te_j\|^2 = \varphi(T^*T).$$

Then for $T \geqq 0$ and unitary U:

$$\varphi(UTU^{-1}) = \varphi(UT^{\frac{1}{2}}T^{\frac{1}{2}}U^{-1}) = \varphi((UT^{\frac{1}{2}})(UT^{\frac{1}{2}})^*) = \varphi((UT^{\frac{1}{2}})^*(UT^{\frac{1}{2}}))$$

$$= \varphi(T^{\frac{1}{2}}U^{-1}UT^{\frac{1}{2}}) = \varphi(T).$$

It follows that φ is independent of the choice of the basis (e_i), because if (f_i) is another basis we can set $f_i = Ue_i$ where U is unitary and then, for $T \geqq 0$:

$$\sum_i (Tf_i \mid f_i) = \sum_i (TUe_i \mid Ue_i) = \sum_i (U^{-1}TUe_i \mid e_i) = \sum_i (Te_i \mid e_i).$$

Proof of axiom (iii): let (T_n) be a filtering family with upper bound T; for all i we have

$$\sup (T_n e_i \mid e_i) = (Te_i \mid e_i)$$

since T is strongly adherent to (T_n) and hence

$$\sup \varphi(T_n) = \varphi(T) .$$

We note that the trace of a projection operator is equal to the Hilbert dimension of the corresponding subspace. The trace φ is obviously faithful; it is finally semi-finite since any positive operator majorizes (Chapter II, § 1, no. 3d) an operator of form kP ($k > 0$, P a non-zero projection operator) and that any projection operator majorizes a finite-dimensional projection operator.

The ideal $\mathfrak{n}$ corresponding to φ is the set of *Hilbert-Schmidt operators* and the ideal $\mathfrak{m}$ is the set of *operators with trace.*

Remark

- It can be proved that the pre-Hilbert space $\mathfrak{n}$ is here Hilbert.
- We mention some remarkable bilateral ideals of $\mathscr{L}(H)$:

$$\hat{\imath} \subset \mathfrak{m} \subset \mathfrak{n} \subset \mathfrak{p}$$

$\hat{\imath}$ = ideal of the operators with finite rank,

$\mathfrak{p}$ = ideal of the compact operators; for the norm topology, $\mathfrak{p}$ is closed and the others are everywhere dense in $\mathfrak{p}$.

§ 4. *Comparison of the projection operators*

We denote by A a von Neumann algebra and by φ a faithful semi-finite trace on A.

Definitions. Two projection operators P and Q in A are said to be *equivalent* ($P \sim Q$) if there exists a partially isometric operator of A which respectively admits P and Q as its initial and final projection operators; we will write $P \prec Q$ if P is equivalent to a projection operator of A majorized by Q; the relation $\prec$ is a preordering relation and one can prove, as for the preordering relation of cardinal numbers, that

$$P \prec Q \quad \text{and} \quad Q \prec P \Rightarrow P \sim Q;$$

we have thus an *order* relation on the set $\mathscr{E}$ of equivalence classes.

Remark. For a systematic study of the ordered set $\mathscr{E}$ see [3].

Lemma 4.3. $P \sim Q \Rightarrow \varphi(P) = \varphi(Q)$; $P \prec Q \Rightarrow \varphi(P) \leqq \varphi(Q)$.

Suppose $P \sim Q$: we have

$$P = V^*V = PV^* \cdot V$$
$$Q = VV^* = V \cdot PV^*;$$

if $\varphi(P)$ and $\varphi(Q)$ are infinite, we are through; if for instance $\varphi(P)$ is finite, $P \in \mathfrak{m}$, $PV^* \in \mathfrak{m}$ and $\varphi(P) = \varphi(Q)$. The sequel is trivial.

Proposition 4.3. If A is a factor, $\mathscr{E}$ is totally ordered.

Let P and Q be non-zero and $\in A$; we will show that there exist projection operators P_1 and Q_1 which are equivalent, non-zero and majorized respectively by P and Q; the proposition will be deduced from this by application of Zorn's lemma. Suppose first that P and Q are non-orthogonal; then

$$QP \neq O$$
$$\text{Image} \quad QP \leqq Q$$
$$\text{Support } QP = \text{Image } (QP)^* = \text{Image } PQ \leqq P$$

and we can hence take $P_1 = \text{Support } QP$ and $Q_1 = \text{Image } QP$. Suppose now that P and Q are orthogonal; let $E = P(H)$; one shows as in Lemma 1.1 that $X_E^A = H$; hence the subspaces $T(E)$ where $T \in A$ are not all orthogonal to Q, and hence neither are the subspaces $U(E)$ where U is unitary and $\in A$; but

$$P_{U(E)} = UP_EU^{-1} \sim P_E.$$

Proposition 4.4. If A is a factor we have $\varphi(P) = \varphi(Q)$ if and only if $P \sim Q$ and $\varphi(P) \leqq (Q)$ if and only if $P \prec Q$.

It remains to be proved that these conditions are necessary; suppose $\varphi(P) \leqq \varphi(Q)$; we have $P \prec Q$ or $Q \prec P$; suppose $Q \prec P$; then $\varphi(P) = \varphi(Q)$ and if $Q \sim Q_1 < P$ we have $\varphi(Q_1) = \varphi(P)$, $\varphi(P - Q_1) = 0$, $P = Q_1$, $P \sim Q$; hence in all cases $P \prec Q$.

The remainder is then trivial.

Lemma 4.4. If A is a continuous factor, any projection operator P of A is the sum of two equivalent orthogonal projection operators of A.

There exists a projection operator Q of A which is non-zero and strictly majorized by P; from the proof of Proposition 4.3. there exist two equivalent projection operators, which are non-zero and majorized respectively by Q and $P - Q$; the proof is completed by using Zorn's lemma. Q. E. D.

The restriction to the set of projection operators of a faithful (resp. faithful and semi-finite if there exist any) trace is called the *relative dimension.*

Theorem 4.4. The set $\varphi(\mathscr{E})$ of the relative dimensions of the projection operators of a factor A is

(i) $\{0, 1, \ldots, n\}$ normalizing φ, if A is of type I_n;
(ii) $\{0, 1, \ldots, +\infty\}$ normalizing φ, if A is of type I_∞;
(iii) $[0, 1]$ normalizing φ, if A is of type II_1;
(iv) $[0, +\infty]$ if A is of type II_∞;
(v) $\{0, +\infty\}$ if A is of type III.

The cases (i) and (ii) are known.

Case (iii); let be φ with $\varphi(1) = 1$; from *Lemma* 4.4, $\varphi(\mathscr{E})$ contains all the numbers $p/2^n$ of $[0,1]$; then let $\alpha \in [0, 1]$; α is the lower bound of a decreasing sequence (α_i) of numbers of the form $p/2^n$; let P_i be a projection operator of relative dimension α_i; there exists (Proposition 4.4) a sequence (Q_i) such that

$$Q_i \sim P_i \quad \text{and} \quad Q_i \leqq Q_{i-1};$$

then

$$\varphi\,(\inf Q_i) = \inf \varphi(Q_i) = \inf \alpha_i = \alpha.$$

Case (iv): any projection operator of A majorizes a non-zero element of A^+ with finite trace, and hence also a projection operator of A with non-zero finite relative dimension; according to Zorn, 1 is the sum of a family of projection operators which are orthogonal two by two and have finite relative dimensions; there exist thus projection operators with arbitrarily large finite relative dimensions; the reasoning carried out in (iii) then shows that $\varphi(\mathscr{E}) = [0, +\infty]$.

Case (v): since φ is not semi-finite, there exists a projection operator P which does not majorize any projection operator with finite relative dimension; if Q is a non-zero projection operator, we have $Q \prec P$ or $P \prec Q$ and in both cases $\varphi(Q)$ is infinite.

Remarks

– Factors of type II lie at the basis of von Neumann's "continuous geometries" – – – geometries where the linear manifolds have continuously varying dimensions.

– The concept of relative dimension in the cases (iii) and (iv) should be compared with the concept of "measure of magnitudes" (cf. [2]).

§ 5. *Example of factor of type II_1*

Let G be a countable group such that for all $s \neq e$ the distinct elements tst^{-1} are in infinite number (for instance the group of transformations $x \to ax + b$ where a and b are rational); for all $s \in G$, let U_s and V_s be the unitary operatore in $L^2(G)$ defined by

$$(U_s\varphi)(t) = \varphi(s^{-1}t)$$

$$(V_s\varphi)(t) = \varphi(ts)$$

(the mappings $s \to U_s$ and $s \to V_s$ are called the "right and left regular representations" of G); let $\mathcal{U}$ and $\mathcal{V}$ be the von Neumann algebras generated respectively by the U_s and the V_s; $\mathcal{U}$ and $\mathcal{V}$ obviously commute; $L^2(G)$ admits an orthonormal basis composed of the functions Ψ_s:

$$\Psi_s(t) = \begin{cases} 1 \text{ if } t = s \\ 0 \text{ otherwise;} \end{cases}$$

in this basis U_s and V_s are represented by matrices $(\alpha_{t,t'})$ and $(\beta_{t,t'})$ with

$$\alpha_{t,t'} = \begin{cases} 1 \text{ if } tt'^{-1} = s \\ 0 \text{ otherwise} \end{cases}$$

$$\beta_{t,t'} = \begin{cases} 1 \text{ if } t^{-1}t' = s \\ 0 \text{ otherwise.} \end{cases}$$

Let $T \in V'$ have matrix $(\gamma_{t,t'})$; expressing that T commutes with the V_s we find that $\gamma_{t,t'}$ depends only on tt'^{-1}, and is hence of the form $\gamma_{t,t'} = \gamma_{tt'^{-1}}$; similarly if $S \in \mathcal{U}'$ we see that its matrix is of the form $\delta_{t,t'} = \delta_{t^{-1}t'}$; now if $T \in \mathcal{U} \cap \mathcal{U}'$, $T \in \mathcal{V}' \cap \mathcal{U}'$ and its matrix is simultaneously of the form $\gamma_{tt'^{-1}}$ and $\delta_{t^{-1}t'}$, i.e.

$$\gamma_{tt'^{-1}} = \delta_{t^{-1}t'} \quad \forall t \text{ and } t'$$

whence

$$\gamma_{t'tt'^{-1}} = \delta_{t^{-1}};$$

for all $t \neq e$, $\gamma_{t'tt'^{-1}}$ assumes the value $\delta_{t^{-1}}$ an infinity of times, which is possible only if $\delta_{t^{-1}} = 0$; T is hence scalar and U is a *factor*.

For all $T \in \mathcal{U}$ with matrix $\gamma_{t,t'} = \gamma_{tt'^{-1}}$, let us set $\varphi(T) = \gamma_e$; we have

$$(T^*T)_e = (TT^*)_e = \sum_t |\gamma_t|^2 \tag{1}$$

which proves that $\varphi(T) \geqq 0$ if $T \geqq 0$ and also that $\varphi(T^*T) = \varphi(TT^*)$; as in § 3 we deduce the axiom (ii) for traces; finally φ is clearly strongly continuous, whence the axiom (iii); φ is hence a trace, which is finite by definition and faithful because of (1).

The factor $\mathcal{U}$ is hence of finite type, and since it is not of type I_n since it contains the U_s which are linearly independent, it is of type II_1.

Remarks. A simple example of a Hilbert algebra can be deduced from this construction. We also mention that one obtains factors of type II_∞ as the tensor products of factors of type II_1 by factors of type I_∞; however the known examples of factors of type III are much more difficult to construct.

TOPOLOGICAL ALGEBRAS
AND HOLOMORPHIC FUNCTIONS

CONTENTS

INTRODUCTION

Our main goal in this Seminar is the determination of the spectra of certain topological algebras connected with the theory of functions of several complex variables, namely:

– for a compact subset X of $\mathfrak{C}^n$, the algebra $\mathscr{P}(X)$ (resp. $\mathscr{R}(X)$) composed of the uniform limits of restrictions to X of polynomials (resp. of rational fractions regular on X) (cf. Theorem 2.1 and Remark 2.2);

– for an analytic complex manifold R, the algebra $\mathscr{O}(R)$ of the functions holomorphic on R (cf. Theorems 2.4 and 2.5);

– for a compact subset X of a manifold R, the algebra $\mathscr{H}(X)$ composed of the uniform limits of restrictions to X of functions holomorphic on R (cf. Theorems 2.3 and 2.6, Corollary 2.3); the algebra $\mathscr{H}_1(X)$ composed of the uniform limits of restrictions to X of functions holomorphic in the neighbourhood of X (cf. Theorem 2.8, Corollaries 2.8, 2.9 and 2.10); finally the algebra $\mathscr{O}(X)$ of the germs of functions holomorphic in the neighbourhood of X (cf. Theorem 2.7 and Corollary 2.7).

In the first chapter we give a few definitions and results concerning topological algebras in general: spectrum or set of the continuous characters, Gelfand transformation, continuity of the said transformation (Proposition 1.1 and 1.6), theorem of Gelfand-Mazur (Corollary 1.1 and Proposition 1.6), inductive and projective limits and their spectra, algebras with continuous inverse. We must note that all the algebras considered in the sequel are either Banach algebras or inductive or projective limits of such algebras; so that we strongly advise the reader to get acquainted with these algebras; he might for instance read the sections 0.4, 0.5, 1.1, 1.3, 1.4, 1.5, 2.1 and 2.2 of the seminar [8]; the present treatise is the logical sequel of [8] and, in particular, completes or makes more precise certain sections of § 6.3 in [8].

It will also be useful to read in [3] the generalities on locally convex spaces as well as what concerns the Hahn-Banach and closed-graph theorems; the fundamental concepts on inductive and projective limits are considered in Appendix I; as regards functions of several complex variables, the definitions and results we will use are contained in Appendix II; we would however recommend reading the sections I, V and XV of [11], as well as [5]. We also point out that many of the results in this seminar which concern complex analytic manifolds can be generalized to complex analytic spaces (cf. [6]).

We will see that the methods of Functional Analysis used here to study functions of several complex variables are much less powerful than others which are more commonly used (sheaves, cohomology, . . .); for instance, in section 2.5, in order to construct the holomorphic envelope of a manifold by means of the theory of Gelfand, we cannot avoid using a theorem by Oka . . .

CHAPTER I

TOPOLOGICAL ALGEBRAS

§ 1.1. *Definitions*

We call a *topological algebra* any complex topological vector space A which is at the same time a commutative algebra with unit such that the bilinear mapping $(x, y) \to xy$ be separately continuous; if this mapping is continuous, we say that A *has continuous multiplication*; we note that if A is a Frechet space it automatically has continuous multiplication (cf. [3], ch. III, § 4, Proposition 2).

An *algebra semi-norm* is a vector-space semi-norm satisfying also $\|xy\| < \|x\| \cdot \|y\|$ and $\|e\| = 1$; any family of algebra semi-norms defines on an algebra a structure of locally convex topological algebra with continuous multiplication; if the family is countable and if A is complete, then A is a *Fréchet space.*

When we talk about a *continuous morphism* $A \to B$, it will always be understood that it transforms the unit of A into that of B.

§ 1.2. *Examples*

(a) The algebra $\mathscr{C}(X)$ of the complex continuous functions on a locally compact topological space X, endowed with the topology of compact convergence; this topology is defined by the family of algebra semi-norms

$$\|f\|_K = \sup |f(x)| \quad \text{for} \quad x \in K$$

where K is an arbitrary compact subset of X; $\mathscr{C}(X)$ is complete and separable; since we have $A \mid K = \mathscr{C}(K)$ for any K, $\mathscr{C}(X)$ is the projective limit of the Banach algebras $\mathscr{C}(K)$ (see the definition of projective limits in § 1.4). If X is a countable union of compact subsets, there exists an increasing sequence (K_n) of compact subsets whose interiors cover X; the topology of $\mathscr{E}(X)$ is then defined by the increasing sequence of semi-norms $\| \|_{K_n}$ and $\mathscr{E}(X)$ is a Fréchet space. We note that if X is not compact, $\mathscr{E}(X)$ is not "banachizable" since its elements are functions which are not all bounded (cf. [8], § 6.1).

b) The algebra $\mathscr{O}(U)$ of the functions holomorphic on an open subset U of $\mathfrak{C}^n$; it is a closed subalgebra of $\mathscr{E}(U)$ and a Fréchet space.

c) Let X be a compact subset of $\mathfrak{C}^n$; we denote by $\mathscr{O}(X)$ the inductive limit of the algebras $\mathscr{O}(U)$, where U is an arbitrary open neighbourhood of X, the mapping $P_{U,V}$: $\mathscr{O}(U) \to \mathscr{O}(V)$ for $U \supset V$ being simply the restriction mapping (see the definition of inductive limits in § 1.4); it is hence the set of the functions holomorphic in the neighbourhood of X split by the following equivalence relation: a function f holomorphic on an open neighbourhood U and a function f' holomorphic on an open neighbourhood U' are equivalent if they coincide on a third open neighbourhood contained in $U \cap U'$; the elements of $\mathscr{O}(X)$ are also called *germs of functions holomorphic in the neighbourhood of* X; in the particular case where $n = 1$ and $X = \{0\}$, a germ is merely a power series with non-zero radius of convergence.

We note that $\mathscr{O}(X)$ can be defined by taking only a decreasing sequence of open neighbourhoods U_n such that $\overline{U_{n+1}}$ is compact and contained in U_n.

The algebra $\mathscr{O}(X)$ is *separated*; indeed, for any positive integer r and any point $a \in X$, the mapping $f \to f^{(r)}(a)$ is a linear form continuous on $\mathscr{O}(X)$ for all U, hence it defines by passing to the limit a continuous linear form on $\mathscr{O}(X)$; moreover these forms separate the elements of $\mathscr{O}(X)$, which is thus separated. $\mathscr{O}(X)$ has continuous multiplication; it is not metrizable, hence non-"banachizable"; let us also mention that it is complete ([19]).

Finally it will be useful to note that $\mathscr{O}(X)$ is also the inductive limit of the *Banach algebras* $H^\infty(U)$ (the algebra of the bounded holomorphic functions on U endowed with the topology of uniform convergence); this follows from the sequence of continuous natural mappings

$$\cdots \to H^\infty(U_n) \to \mathscr{O}(U_n) \to H^\infty(U_{n+1}) \to \mathscr{O}(U_{n+1}) \to \cdots$$

§ 1.3. *Continuous characters*

Contrarily to the conventions of [8], §0.5, we will consider here only the *continuous* characters of a topological algebra A, i.e. the continuous morphisms of A into $\mathfrak{C}$; their kernels are *closed* maximal ideals of A, and we have thus an *injective* mapping of the set of continuous characters into that of the closed maximal ideals; again in disagreement with [8], we will call *spectrum* $\hat{A}$ of A the set of continuous characters of A endowed with the topology of simple convergence; $\hat{A}$ is a *separated* topological space. The *Gelfand transformation* will be the morphism $x \to \hat{x}$ of A into $\mathscr{C}(\hat{A})$ defined by $\hat{x}(\chi) = \chi(x)$; the topology of $\hat{A}$ is obviously the least fine topology which makes the functions $\hat{x}$ continuous.

Proposition 1.1. If A is a Frechet space (or, more generally, a barreled space), the Gelfand transformation is a continuous morphism when we endow $\mathscr{C}(\hat{A})$ with the topology of compact convergence.

Indeed, in this case any compact subset of $\hat{A}$ is equicontinuous ([3], ch. IV, § 2, Theorem 1).

We note that for any $x \in A$ and any $\chi \in \hat{A}$ we have $\chi(x) \in \operatorname{sp} x$.

We will call *transpose* of a continuous morphism $u : A \to B$ the continuous mapping ${}^t u : \hat{B} \to \hat{A}$ defined by ${}^t u(\chi) = \chi \circ u$; if $\operatorname{Im} u$ is everywhere dense in B, ${}^t u$ is *injective*. We note that for any $x \in A$ we have $\widehat{u(x)} = \hat{x} \circ {}^t u$.

Remark 1.1. The spectrum considered here of an element x of A can be empty or even non-closed; to counter this disadvantage, L. Waelbroek proposed in [20] (see also [4]) to modify the definition of sp x, which would then be the complement of the set of λ_0 such that the function $\lambda \to (x - \lambda e)^{-1}$ is defined and bounded (in the sense of the topological vector spaces) in the neighbourhood of λ_0; one shows that sp x defined in this way is closed and non-empty; further one says that x is regular if $(x - \lambda e)^{-1}$ is defined and bounded in the neighbourhood of the point at infinity; then sp x is compact; the regular elements form a subalgebra A_r which we do not topologize; for $x \in A_r$, sp x is merely the spectrum $\operatorname{sp}_{A_r} x$ taken in the usual sense, which is thus compact; one considers the characters of A_r and one obtains a Gelfand transformation with good properties. We will not adopt this viewpoint, because the spectrum of A_r can be much more complicated than that of A; for instance in the case of example (a) the regular elements are the bounded functions, i.e. $A_r = \mathscr{C}^\infty(X)$; the characters of the non-topological algebra A_r are those of the Banach algebra $\mathscr{C}^\infty(X)$ and their set is rather complicated (cf. [8], § 1.5); in the case of example (b) we have $A_r = H^\infty(U)$ and we can make a similar remark.

Remark 1.2. In [18] one will find a study of normed countable topological algebras, mainly devoted to involutive algebras, to which the theory of involutive Banach algebras is generalized.

Remark 1.3. It is not without interest to set the following algebraic result in parallel with the present theory: Hilbert's Nullstellensatz; let A be the (non-topological) algebra of the polynomials in n indeterminates over $\mathfrak{C}$; then if some elements $f_1, \ldots, f_p$ of A have no common zero, there exist elements $g_1, \ldots, g_p$ of A such that $\sum f_i g_i = 1$; this, together with the fact that A is noetherian, implies that any maximal ideal of A is the kernel of a character and that all characters are of the form $f \to f(x)$ where $x \in \mathfrak{C}^n$.

§ 1.4. *Spectra of projective or injective limits of locally convex algebras*

An *inductive system* of locally convex topological algebras is an inductive system of locally convex topological vector spaces A_i (cf. Appendix I), each A_i being a topological algebra and each $P_{i,j}$ a continuous morphism; in the space $\varinjlim A_i$, multiplication is defined in the same manner as addition, and it is easy to see that $\varinjlim A_i$ becomes thus a topological algebra; moreover if multiplication is continuous in each A_i, it is also continuous in $\varinjlim A_i$.

The definition of projective limits presents no more difficulties once we know Appendix I: the mappings $P_{i,j} : A_j \to A_i$ are still assumed to be continuous morphisms; the elements of the space $\varprojlim A_i$ are families $(x_i)_{i \in I}$ where $x_i \in A_i$ and the product of two such elements is performed component by component. We are going to study to what extent the spectrum of a projective limit is the inductive limit of the spectra and vice versa.

Proposition 1.2. Let A be the projective limit of a projective system of locally convex algebras A_i with the continuous morphisms $P_{i,j} : A_j$

$\to A_i$ and $P_i : A \to A_i$; we assume Im P_i is everywhere dense in A_i for all i; the topological spaces $X_i = \hat{A}_i$ form an inductive system with continuous mappings $R_{i,j} = {}^tP_{i,j} : X_i \to X_j$; let be $X = \varinjlim X_i$ and, for all i, R_i the canonical mapping $X_i \to X$. There exists a bijective continuous mapping L from X onto $\hat{A}$ transforming each $\chi \in X$ into the charactei $L(\chi)$ of A defined by

$$(L(\chi))(x) = \chi_i(x_i)$$

for any i and $\chi_i \in X_i$ satisfying $R_i(\chi_i) = \chi$.

Proof. We have continuous mappings $L_i = {}^tP_i : X_i \to \hat{A}$ forming an inductive system, whence a continuous mapping $L : X \to \hat{A}$ such that $L \circ R_i = L_i$ for all i; i.e. if $\chi = R_i(\chi_i) \in X$ and if $x \in A$, we have

$$(L(\chi))\ (x) = (L_i(\chi_i))\ (x) = \chi_i(P_i(x)) = \chi_i(x_i).$$

L is injective because if $L(\chi) = L(\chi')$, we can write $\chi = R_i(\chi_i)$ and $\chi' = R_i(\chi_i')$ and we have $\chi_i(x_i) = \chi_i'(x_i)$ for all $x_i \in$ Im P_i, hence $\chi_i = \chi_i'$ and $\chi = \chi'$. L is surjective; indeed, let $\sigma \in A$; we know (appendix I, § 4) that there exists an index i and a continuous linear form χ_i on A_i such that $\sigma = \chi_i \circ P_i$; χ_i is multiplicative on Im P_i, hence $\chi_i \in \hat{A}_i$ and we have

$$\sigma = {}^tP_i(\chi_i) = L_i(\chi_i) = L(R_i(\chi_i)).$$

Remark. 1.4. L is not necessarily bicontinuous, even if the A_i are Banach algebras and the $P_{i,j}$ have norm 1. Let indeed E be a non-regular separable topological space, whose topology is finer than a compact topology (cf. [1], chapter I, § 8, exercise 20, c)); the algebra $\mathscr{C}(E)$ is separating; following nearly word for word the reasoning in [2], § 4, Theorem 2, one shows that any continuous function on a compact subset K of E extends to a continuous function on E; $\mathscr{C}(E)$ is thus the projective limit of the algebras $\mathscr{C}(K)$ and we know that $\widehat{\mathscr{C}(K)}$ is homeomorphic to K (cf. [8], § 2.1); we have an obvious bijective continuous mapping $\varinjlim K \to E$ and a canonical bijective continuous mapping $T : E \to \widehat{\mathscr{C}(E)}$ (cf. § 1.6); the composed mapping $\varinjlim K \to \widehat{\mathscr{C}(E)}$ is precisely our mapping L; T is not bicontinuous since $\widehat{\mathscr{C}(E)}$ is uniformizable whereas E is not; hence L is not bicontinuous.

Proposition 1.3. Let A be the inductive limit of an inductive system of locally convex algebras A_i with the continuous morphisms $P_{i,j} : A_i$

$\to A_j$ and $P_i : A_i \to A$; the topological spaces $X_i = \hat{A}_i$ form a projective system with continuous mappings $R_{i,j} = {}^tP_{i,j} : X_j \to X_i$; let be $X \to \varprojlim X_i$ and, for all i, R_i the canonical mapping $X \to X_i$. There exists a homeomorphism L from X onto $\hat{A}$ transforming any $\chi \in X$ into the character $L(\chi)$ defined by

$$(L(\chi))(x) = \chi_i(x_i)$$

for any i and $x_i \in A_i$ verifying $P_i(x_i) = x$.

Proof. We have continuous mappings $M_i = {}^tP_i : \hat{A} \to X_i$ forming a projective system, whence a continuous mapping $M : \hat{A} \to X$ such that $R_i \circ M = {}^tP_i$ for all i; i.e. for $\sigma \in \hat{A}$ we have

$$(M(\sigma))_i = \sigma \circ P_i \tag{1}$$

M is

- trivially injective, from (1)
- surjective: indeed, let $\chi = (\chi_i) \in X$; it is an inductive system of continuous linear mappings $A_i \to \mathfrak{C}$, hence there exists a continuous linear mapping $\sigma : A \to \mathfrak{C}$ such that $\sigma \circ P_i = \chi_i$ for all i; σ is necessarily a character and we have $\chi = M(\sigma)$; we note that if we set $\sigma = L(\chi)$ we have for all $x = P_i(x_i) \in A$

$$(L(\chi))(x) = \chi_i(x_i);$$

- bicontinuous: indeed, if χ converges to χ^0, each χ_i converges to χ_i^0 and $L(\chi)$ is simply convergent.

Remark 1.5. Assume that the A_i are *Banach algebras*; we can define their limit in the sense of the categorie of the Banach algebras: we endow A with the semi-norm

$$\|x\| = \inf \|x_i\| \quad \text{for all } x_i \text{ verifying} \quad P_i(x_i) = x,$$

we pass to the quotient and we complete; we obtain thus a Banach algebra A^*; we have a continuous morphism $U : A \to A^*$, inductive limit of the canonical morphisms $A_i \to A^*$; ${}^tU$ is injective since Im U is everywhere dense in A^*; it is surjective, because let $\chi \in \hat{A}$; for all i, $P_i \circ \chi$ is a character of A_i, hence of norm 1, i.e. if $x = P_i(x_i) \in A$ we have

$$|\chi(x)| = |(P_i \circ \chi)(x_i)| \leqq \|x_i\|$$

hence

$$|\chi(x)| \leqq \|x\|;$$

we see that χ does indeed come from a character of A^*. We have hence proved that ${}^tU$ is a *homeomorphism* from $\widehat{A^*}$ onto $\hat{A}$.

Remark 1.6. In the case of projective limits there is also a concept in the sense of the category of the Banach algebras: we take the subalgebra of A composed of the families (x_i) such that sup $\|x_i\| < +\infty$; with the norm $\|(x_i)\| = \sup \|x_i\|$, it is a Banach algebra A^*; but its spectrum can be very different from that of A: for instance $\mathscr{C}(X)$ (X a locally compact space) is a projective limit of the $\mathscr{C}(K)$; the projective limit in the sense of the Banach algebras is $\mathscr{C}^\infty(X)$!

§ 1.5. *Topologies defined by families of algebra semi-norms*

The topological algebras in question are those whose completion is a projective limit of Banach algebras; they are also called "locally *m*-convex algebras" (cf. [12]).

Proposition 1.4. Let A be a topological algebra whose topology is defined by a filtering family $(\| \|_i)_{i\in I}$ of algebra semi-norms; for all i, let A_i be the corresponding completed Banach algebra and P_i the canonical continuous morphism from A into A_i.

(i) Any closed ideal of A is contained in a closed maximal ideal;

(ii) Any closed maximal ideal is the kernel of a character.

(iii) For all i, ${}^tP_i$ is a homeomorphism of $\hat{A}_i$ onto a compact subset K_i of $\hat{A}$ and we have $\hat{A} = \bigcup K_i$.

Proof. The first assertion of (iii) is trivial since Im P_i is everywhere dense in A_i. Let us now consider a closed ideal J of A; there exists a neighbourhood of e of the form $\{x : \|x - e\|_i < \varepsilon\}$ disjoint from J; $P_i(J)$ is an ideal of Im P_i disjoint from the ball of radius ε and center e in A_i; its adherence $\overline{P_i(J)}$ is an ideal of A_i, and hence is contained in the kernel of a character χ of A_i; hence J is contained in the kernel of the character $\chi \circ P_i = {}^tP_i(\chi)$ of A; whence (i). If J is maximal, we necessarily have $J = \text{Ker}\,({}^tP_i(\chi))$; whence (ii); finally if σ is a character of A, its kernel will also be the kernel of a character of form ${}^tP_i(\chi)$, hence $\sigma = {}^tP_i(\chi)$; whence the second assertion of (iii); we note that this assertion also follows from Proposition 1.2.

Corollary 1.1. If A is separated and is a field, it is isomorphic to $\mathbb{C}$. Because $\{0\}$ is a closed ideal, hence maximal, hence the kernel of a character.

§ 1.6. *Topological function algebras*

Let X be a topological space and A an algebra of continuous complex functions containing the constant functions and endowed with a topology finer than that of simple of convergence; by associating to each point x of X the character of $A : f \to f(x)$, we define a continuous mapping, said to be *canonical*, $T : X \to \hat{A}$; T is injective if and only if A separates the points of X.

Example (a): T is a *homeomorphism* from X onto $\widehat{\mathscr{C}(X)}$. Indeed T is obviously continuous and injective; to show that it is surjective we can either

– apply the proposition 1.2;

– note that any character of $\mathscr{C}(X)$ is continuous for one of the seminorms $\| \|_K$ (cf. [3], Chapter II, § 5, Proposition 9), hence proceeds from a character of $\mathscr{C}(K)$, which is necessarily of the form $f \to f(x)$ where $x \in K$;

– note that the subalgebra $\mathscr{C}_0(X)$ of $\mathscr{C}(X)$ composed of the functions equal to zero at infinity is everywhere dense in $\mathscr{C}(X)$; let then χ be a character of $\mathscr{C}(X)$; $\chi \mid \mathscr{C}_0(X)$ is a character of $\mathscr{C}_0(X)$, and hence, from [8], § 1.5, of form $f \to f(x)$ where $x \in X$.

Finally to show that T is bicontinuous it suffices to show that any open neighbourhood U of a point x_0 contains a neighbourhood defined by a condition

$$|f(x) - f(x_0)| < \varepsilon \quad \text{with} \quad f \in \mathscr{C}(X);$$

now there exists a function $f \in \mathscr{C}(X)$ equal to 1 at x_0 and to 0 on $X - U$ and we can take $\varepsilon = \frac{1}{2}$.

Remark 1.7. One can show that T is bijective and continuous even if X is not locally compact, assuming only that $\mathscr{C}(X)$ separates the points of X; and that T is a homeomorphism if and only if X is uniformizable.

§ 1.7. *Algebras with continuous inverse*

Definition. A locally convex topological algebra is said to have *continuous inverse* if the mapping $x \to x^{-1}$ is defined on a neighbourhood of e and continuous at e. We will note that we assume neither that the algebra be separated nor that it have continuous multiplication.

The algebras in examples (a) and (b) are not with continuous inverse: for (a) it is obvious; for (b) let us take $U = \mathfrak{C}$ and show that for any positive r and a there exists a function f holomorphic on $\mathfrak{C}$ which verifies $|f(z) - 1| \leqq a$ for all z of modulus $\leqq r$ and which equals zero at least once; there exists a $b > 0$ such that $|z| \leqq b$ inplies $|e^z - 1| \leqq a/2$; the function $f(z) = e^{bz/r} + a/2$ answers the question.

Any commutative Banach algebra has continuous inverse (cf. [8], Theorem 1.1); more generally:

Proposition 1.5. Let A be the inductive limit of a sequence (A_i) $(i = 1, 2, \ldots)$ of commutative Banach algebras with morphisms $P_{i,j}: A_i \to A_j$ of norm 1; then A has continuous inverse.

We denote by $B_{i,r}$ the open ball with center 0 and radius r in A_i, and by P_i the canonical morphism from A_i into A; the set $\bigcup_i P_i(B_{i,1}) = U$ is a neighbourhood of 0 in A because it is convex, balanced and $P_i^{-1}(U)$ is a neighbourhood of 0 in A_i for all i; moreover any element of $e + U$ is invertible and if $x \in U$, $(e - x)^{-1}$ is the sum of the series $\sum_0^\infty x^n$. It remains to show that in A the mapping $x \to x^{-1}$ in continuous at e.

We will first prove the following assertion:

(A) Any convex neighbourhood V of 0 in A contains a neighbourhood W such that $x \in W$ implies $2^{n-1}x^n \in W$ for all integers $n \geqq 1$.

For all i, $P_i^{-1}(V)$ contains a ball B_{i,r_i} of radius $r_i \leqq \frac{1}{2}$; let us set $W' = \bigcup_i P_i(B_{i,r_i})$ and denote by W the convex hull of W'; W is a neighbourhood of 0 contained in V; let $x \in W$; x is of the form

$$x = \sum_{s=1}^{p} a_s x_s$$

with $0 \leqq a_s \leqq 1$, $\sum a_s = 1$ and $x_s \in W'$; the element

$$2^{n-1}x^n = \sum_{s_1 \ldots s_n} a_{s_1} \ldots a_{s_n} \cdot 2^{n-1} \cdot x_{s_1} \ldots x_{s_n}$$

is the barycentre of the elements $2^{n-1} \cdot x_{s_1} \ldots x_{s_n}$ and the problem reduces to proving that these elements belong to W'; each x_{s_q} is of the form

$$x_{s_q} = P_{i_q}(y_{i_q}) \quad \text{where} \quad y_{i_q} \in B_{i_q, r_{i_q}};$$

to fix our ideas let us suppose that $i_1 \geqq i_q$ for any $q = 1, \ldots, n$; let us set

$$z_q = P_{i_q, i_1}(y_{i_q}) \in A_{i_1};$$

we then have

$$x_{s_q} = P_{i_1}(z_q)$$

$$\|z_1\| \leqq r_{i_1}$$

and for $q = 2, \ldots, n$

$$\|z_q\| \leqq \|y_{i_q}\| \leqq \tfrac{1}{2};$$

then

$$\|2^{n-1} \cdot z_1 \ldots z_n\| \leqq 2^{n-1} \cdot r_{i_1} \cdot \tfrac{1}{2}^{n-1} = r_{i_1}$$

that is

$$2^{n-1} \cdot z_1 \ldots z_n \in B_{i_1, r_{i_1}}$$

whence

$$2^{n-1} \cdot x_{s_1} \ldots x_{s_n} = P_{i_1}(2^{n-1} \cdot z_1 \ldots z_n) \in W';$$

this proves assertion (A).

Let now Z be a balanced convex closed neighbourhood of 0 in A; let us set $V = \frac{1}{2} Z$ and construct W with the property of A; let $x \in W \cap U$; $(e - x)^{-1} - e$ is the limit of $x + x^2 + \ldots + x^n$ for $n \to +\infty$; we can write

$$x + x^2 + \cdots x^n = u_1/2 + u_2/4 + \cdots u_n/2^n$$

with $u_1, u_2 \ldots u_n \in Z$; since Z is convex and balanced, $x + x^2 + \ldots + x^n \in Z$; finally since Z is closed, $(e - x)^{-1} - e \in Z$. Q. E. D.

It follows in particular that the algebra $\mathcal{O}(X)$ in the example (c) has continuous inverse.

Study of algebras with continuous inverse

Let A be an algebra with continuous inverse.

Lemma 1.1. The set E of the invertible elements of A is open and the mapping $x \to x^{-1}$ is continuous in it.

Because let $x \in E$; $x + y = x\,(e + x^{-1}y)$ is invertible if y is sufficiently small; then the element

$$(x + y)^{-1} - x^{-1} = x^{-1}(e + x^{-1}y)^{-1} - x^{-1} = x^{-1}((e + x^{-1}y)^{-1} - e)$$

tends to 0 together with y.

Lemma 1.2. The closure of an ideal is an ideal; in particular all maximal ideals are closed (we recall that "distinct from A" is always understood in the word "ideal").

Because every ideal is contained in the closed set $A - E$.

Lemma 1.3. The spectrum of an arbitrary element x of A is compact; it is furthermore non-void if we assume A is separated.

First sp x is closed as the inverse image of $A - E$ under the continuous mapping $\lambda \to x - \lambda e$; it is relatively compact because if λ is sufficiently large x/λ is arbitrarily small and $x - \lambda e = -\lambda\,(e - x/\lambda)$ is invertible. On the other hand the mapping

$$\lambda \to R(x, \lambda) = (x - \lambda e)^{-1}$$

from $\mathfrak{C}$ − sp x into A is continuous and verifies

$$R(x, \lambda) - R(x, \lambda') = (\lambda - \lambda') \cdot R(x, \lambda) \cdot R(x, \lambda')$$

whence it follows readily that it is holomorphic; moreover it is holomorphic at the point at infinity; let us assume that sp x is void; for any linear continuous form f on A the holomorphic function $\lambda \to f(R(x, \lambda))$ is constant by virtue of the Liouville theorem; if we assume moreover that A is separated the continuous linear forms on A separate the elements of A (Hahn-Banach theorem); in this case the function $\lambda \to R(x, \lambda)$ is hence constant, say $(x - \lambda e)\, a = e$ for all λ; in particular $xa = e$, which implies that $-\lambda a = e$ which is absurd.

Lemma 1.4. If A is a field and is separated, it is isomorphic to $\mathfrak{C}$.

For any $x \in A$ there exists indeed a complex number λ such that $x - \lambda e$ is not invertible; but this implies that $x = \lambda e$.

Lemma 1.5. Any maximal ideal I of A is the kernel of a character.

It can readily be verified that A/I has continuous inverse; it is separated since I is closed, and it is a field since I is maximal; it is hence isomorphic to $\mathfrak{C}$.

Lemma 1.6. A has at least one character.

It has indeed at least one maximal ideal by virtue of the Krull theorem.

Lemma 1.7. The spectrum of an element x of A is the set of the numbers $\chi(x)$ where χ runs through the set of characters of A (not assumed to be continuous a priori).

If χ is a character of A the element $x - \chi(x) \cdot e$ is annihilated by χ and thus cannot be invertible; conversely if $\lambda e \in$ sp x the element $x - \lambda e$ is contained in an ideal hence in a maximal ideal i.e. it is annihilated by a character.

Lemma 1.8. The spectrum of an arbitrary element of A is non-void; if A is a field, it is isomorphic to $\mathfrak{C}$.

The first assertion is trivial; the second is deduced from it in the same manner as in Lemma 1.4.

Lemma 1.9. For any $x \in A$ let us set $\nu(x) = \sup |\lambda|$ for all the $\lambda \in \operatorname{sp} x$; then $\lim_{x \to 0} \nu(x) = 0$.

We must show that for any $\varepsilon > 0$ there is a balanced neighbourhood V of 0 in A such that $x \in V$ and $|\lambda| \geqq \varepsilon$ imply that $x - \lambda e$ is invertible; let W be a neighbourhood of 0 such that $y \in W$ implies that $e - y$ is invertible and let $V = \varepsilon W$; if $x \in V$ $x/\lambda = x/\varepsilon \cdot \varepsilon/\lambda \in W$ and $x - \lambda e = -\lambda\,(e - x/\lambda)$ is invertible.

Lemma 1.10. The set $\hat{A}$ of the characters of A is equicontinuous; in particular any character of A is continuous.

For any $x \in A$ and any $\chi \in \hat{A}$ we have indeed $|\chi(x)| \leqq \nu(x)$.

Lemma 1.11. $\hat{A}$ is compact for the topology of simple convergence.

Because $\hat{A}$ is a closed subset of $\mathfrak{C}^A = \prod_{x \in A} \mathfrak{C}$ and is contained in $\prod_{x \in A} \operatorname{sp} x$.

Lemma 1.12. The Gelfand transformation is a continuous morphism from A into $\mathscr{C}(\hat{A})$ endowed with the topology of uniform convergence.

This follows immediately from Lemma 1.10.

In short we can state the

Proposition 1.6. If A is an algebra with continuous inverse, the characters of A (automatically continuous) correspond bijectively to the maximal ideals of A (automatically closed); the spectrum of an arbitrary element x is compact, void and equal to the set of the numbers $\chi(x)$ for $\chi \in \hat{A}$; $\hat{A}$ is compact, and equicontinuous; the Gelfand transformation is a continuous morphism from A into $\mathscr{C}(\hat{A})$ endowed with the topology of uniform convergence; finally if A is a field, it is isomorphic to $\mathfrak{C}$.

CHAPTER II

TOPOLOGICAL ALGEBRAS AND HOLOMORPHIC FUNCTIONS

§ 2.1. *Banach algebras of functions in $\mathfrak{C}^n$: generalities*

We can consider various types of Banach algebras of functions in $\mathfrak{C}^n$ related to the holomorphic functions:

1) for a compact subset $X \subset \mathfrak{C}^n$

– $\mathcal{P}(X)$, closure in $\mathcal{C}(X)$ of the set of the restrictions of polynomials

– $\mathcal{R}(X)$, closure in $\mathcal{C}(X)$ of the set of the restrictions of rational fractions regular on X.

– $\mathcal{H}_1(X)$, closure in $\mathcal{C}(X)$ of the set of the restrictions of holomorphic functions in the neighbourhood of X; we have obviously

$$\mathcal{P}(x) \subset \mathcal{R}(x) \subset \mathcal{H}_1(x) \subset \mathcal{C}(x);$$

2) again for a compact subset, an algebra which is between $\mathcal{H}_1(X)$ and $\mathcal{C}(X)$: that of the continuous functions on X holomorphic on its interior; however the study of its spectrum seems definitely more difficult;

3) for an open subset $U \subset \mathfrak{C}^n$ the algebra $H^\infty(U)$ of the bounded holomorphic functions on U; same remark.

We are now going to study $\mathcal{P}(X)$ and $\mathcal{R}(X)$ postponing $\mathcal{H}_1(X)$ till later (cf. § 2.8.) and the two others indefinitely.

§ 2.2. *Study of* $\mathscr{P}(X)$ *and* $\mathscr{R}(X)$

We will merely recall some definitions and results which are stated in [8], § 6.3.

Definitions. A compact subset X of $\mathfrak{C}^n$ is said to be *polynomially convex* if for any $z^0 \in \mathfrak{C}^n - X$ there is a polynomial P with complex coefficients satisfying

$$|P(z^0)| > \sup_{z \in X} |P(z)|;$$

this amounts to saying that X is compact and defined by conditions of the form

$$|P_i(z)| \leqq k_i$$

where the P_i are polynomials; we note that the family is in general infinite.

Let X be an arbitrary compact subset of $\mathfrak{C}^n$; the set X' of the z^0 satisfying

$$|P(z^0)| \leqq \sup_{z \in X} |P(z)| \quad \text{for any polynomial } P$$

is called the *polynomial convex hull of* X; it is the smallest polynomially convex compact subset containing X.

In the case where $n = 1$ a compact set X is polynomially convex if and only if $\mathfrak{C} - X$ is connected (cf. [8], Corollary 2.3); and to obtain the polynomial convex hull of an arbitrary compact set X, we add to X the bounded connected components of its complement in other words we "fill the holes".

In the general case, the polynomial convex hull of a compact set X is the set of points z with the following property: if $(H_t)_{0 \leqq t \leqq \infty}$ is a continuous family of algebraic hypersurfaces which tend to infinity as t tends to infinity and of which one contains z one at least meets X (cf. [17]).

Theorem 2.1. For any compact subset X of $\mathfrak{C}^n$, $\widehat{\mathscr{P}(X)}$ is identical to the polynomial convex hull of X; more precisely there is a homeomorphism from X' onto $\widehat{\mathscr{P}(X)}$ which transforms any point z of X' into the character of $\mathscr{P}(X)$ defined by $\chi(P \mid X) = P(z)$ for all polynomials P.

Cf. [8], § 6.3, no. 2.

Theorem 2.2. If X is a polynomially convex compact subset of $\mathfrak{C}^n$, we have $\mathscr{P}(X) = \mathscr{H}_1(X)$; in other words any function holomorphic in the neighbourhood of X is a uniform limit on X of polynomials.

Cf. [8], § 6.3, no. 4.

Corollary 2.1. If X is an arbitrary compact subset of $\mathfrak{C}^n$, any connected component of X' meets X; in particular if X is connected, so is X'.

Let us suppose indeed that there is a connected component E of X' which does not meet X; there exists a function f holomorphic in the neighbourhood of X', equal to 1 on E and to 0 on $X' - E$; there exists thus a sequence of polynomials converging uniformly to 1 on E and to 0 on $X' - E$, hence on X - - - which is absurd.

Remark 2.1. If $n = 1$ the converse of Theorem 2.2 is true; because, let us suppose that $\mathfrak{C} - X$ has a non-void bounded connected component U; any function on X which is a uniform limit of restrictions of polynomials can be extended holomorphically in U by virtue of the maximum principle; now, for $z^0 \in U$, the function $z \to 1/(z - z^0)$ is holomorphic in the neighbourhood of X, but cannot be extended holomorphically in U, because if f were such an extension we would have $(z - z^0) \cdot f(z) - 1 = 0$ on X, hence on U.

Remark 2.2. We can build up a completely analogous theory for the algebra $\mathscr{R}(X)$ and for the rationally convex compact subsets of $\mathfrak{C}^n$, i.e. such that for any $z^0 \in \mathfrak{C}^n - X$ there is a rational fraction R regular on $X \cup \{z^0\}$ and satisfying

$$|R(z^0)| > \sup_{z \in X} |R(z)|;$$

in the case $n = 1$ it is easy to see that any compact subset is rationally convex; in the general case the rational convex hull of an arbitrary compact subset X is the set of points z such that any algebraic hypersurface containing z meets X (cf. [17]). The two previous theorems have the following analogues:

- for any compact set X, $\widehat{\mathscr{R}(X)}$ is identical with the rational convex hull of X;

- if X is rationally convex we have $\mathscr{R}(X) = \mathscr{H}_1(X)$.

§ 2.3. *Banach algebras of functions in a manifold*

For the definition of complex analytic manifolds, see Appendix II; all the manifolds considered here will be assumed to be a countable union of compact sets.

Given a manifold R we can consider various types of Banach algebras connected with the holomorphic functions: first, for any compact set $X \subset R$;

– $\mathcal{H}(X)$, closure in $\mathcal{C}(X)$ of the set of restrictions of holomorphic functions on R

– $\mathcal{H}_1(X)$, closure in $\mathcal{C}(X)$ of the set of restrictions of holomorphic functions in the neighbourhood of X; we have obviously

$$\mathcal{H}(X) \subset \mathcal{H}_1(X) \subset \mathcal{C}(X).$$

We can also consider two other types of algebras as in § 2.1; we will study $\mathcal{H}(X)$ in the present section (see also § 2.6) and $\mathcal{H}_1(X)$ in § 2.8.

Definition. We will say – this is not standard terminology – that a compact subset X of a manifold R is *holomorphically convex* if for all $y \in R - X$ there is a function f holomorphic on R and satisfying

$$|f(y)| > \sup_{x \in X} |f(x)|;$$

this amounts to saying that X is compact and defined by conditions of the form

$$|f_i(x)| \leq k_i$$

where the f_i are holomorphic on R; we note that the family is in general infinite.

If now X is an arbitrary compact set, we will denote by X' and call *holomorphic convex hull* of X the set of points y satisfying

$$|f(y)| \leq \sup_{x \in X} |f(x)| \quad \text{for any function } f \text{ holomorphic on } R;$$

it is essential to note that X' is in general *not compact.*

Theorem 2.3. If X is a holomorphically convex subset of a manifold R, the canonical mapping from X into $\widehat{\mathcal{H}(X)}$ is surjective; in other words any character of $\mathcal{H}(X)$ is of the form $f \to f(x)$ where $x \in X$.

Proof. It will be done in two steps, examining first a particular case.

a) Particular case.

Let us suppose that X is the set of points x of an open set U satisfying the conditions $|f_i(x)| \leqq 1$, $i = 1, \ldots, k$, where the f_i are holomorphic functions on R such that for any $r : 1 \leqq r \leqq 2$, the set X_r fo the points of U satisfying $|f_i(x)| \leqq r$ is compact.

1) We have then $X = X_1$; we denote by $\check{X}_2$ the set of points of U satisfying $|f_i(x)| < 2$. Let G be the set of holomorphic functions on R which are strictly smaller than 1 on X_1 and than 2 on X_2; it is clear that $G \mid X_1$ generates $\mathscr{H}(X_1)$ as a subalgebra. For any $r : 1 \leqq r \leqq 2$, we denote by D_r the set of points of $\mathfrak{C}^k \times \mathfrak{C}^G$ all the coordinates of which have modulus $< r$; let S be the mapping from $\check{X}_2$ into D_2 defined by

$$S(x) = ((f_i(x))_{i=1\ldots k}, (g(x))_{g \in G});$$

the set $B = S(X_1)$ is compact and contained in $\bar{D}_1$.

2) We will show that *B is the set of the common zeros of a set of elements of $\mathscr{P}(\bar{D}_1)$* ($\mathscr{P}(\bar{D}_1)$ denotes the closure in $\mathscr{E}(\bar{D}_1)$ of the set of restrictions of polynomials).

For an arbitrary finite subset E of G we denote by D'_r the open polydisc of center 0 and of radius r in $\mathfrak{C}^k \times \mathfrak{C}^E$ and pr_E the projection of D_2 in D'_2; $\mathrm{pr}_E \circ S$ is a holomorphic mapping from $\check{X}_2$ into D'_2, which maps X_1 onto $\mathrm{pr}_E(B) = \mathrm{pr}_E(S(\check{X}_2)) \cap \bar{D}'_1$. The mapping $\mathrm{pr}_E \circ S$ is proper: if indeed K is a compact subset of D'_2, it is contained in a $\bar{D}'_r$ with $r < 2$; then $(\mathrm{pr}_E \circ S)^{-1}(K)$ is contained in X_r, and is hence compact. It follows cf. [16], Theorem 3.3) that $\mathrm{pr}_E(S(\check{X}_2))$ is an analytic subset of D'_2, hence (cf. Appendix II, § 1) that it is the set of common zeros of a set of holomorphic functions on D'_2; since such a function is a limit of polynomials uniformly on $\bar{D}'_1$, $\mathrm{pr}_E(B)$ is the set of common zeros of a set of elements of $\mathscr{P}(\bar{D}'_1)$; then the set $\mathrm{pr}_E^{-1}(\mathrm{pr}_E(B)) \cap \bar{D}_1$ is the set of common zeros of a set of elements of $\mathscr{P}(\bar{D}_1)$; finally the same is true for the set

$$\bigcap_E \mathrm{pr}_E^{-1}(\mathrm{pr}_E(B)) \cap \bar{D}_1 = B \cap \bar{D}_1 = B.$$

3) Let us now prove that *any character of* $\mathcal{P}(B)$ *is of the form* $f \to f(y_0)$ where $y_0 \in B$.

First, any character χ of $\mathcal{P}(\overline{D}_1)$ is of the form $g \to g(z_0)$ where $z_0 \in \overline{D}_1$; because, let u_i be the value of χ on the coordinate function $z \to z_i$; we have $|u_i| \leqq 1$, that is $u = (u_i) \in \overline{D}_1$; further $\chi(g) = g(u)$ for any polynomial g, hence, by continuity, for all $g \in \mathcal{P}(\overline{D}_1)$. Let now σ be a character of $\mathcal{P}(B)$; combining it with the canonical mapping: $\mathcal{P}(\overline{D}_1) \to \mathcal{P}(B)$, we obtain a character of $\mathcal{P}(\overline{D}_1)$, which corresponds to a point z_0 of $\overline{D}_1$; z_0 belongs to B because if it did not there would exist a function of $\mathcal{P}(\overline{D}_1)$ which is zero on B and non-zero in z_0; we have hence $\sigma(f \mid B) = f(z_0)$ for any polynomial f, then for any $f \in \mathcal{P}(B)$, by continuity.

4) There is an *isomorphism* L *from* $\mathcal{P}(B)$ *onto* $\mathcal{H}(X_1)$ *such that* $L(p \mid B) = p \circ S$ for any polynomial p on $\mathfrak{C}^k \times \mathfrak{C}^G$.

The mapping $p \mid B \to p \circ S \in \mathcal{H}(X_1)$ is indeed isometric, hence extends into an isomorphism from $\mathcal{P}(B)$ onto a closed subalgebra of $\mathcal{H}(X_1)$, which is equal to $\mathcal{H}(X_1)$ since it contains $G \mid X_1$.

5) Let χ be a character of $\mathcal{H}(X_1)$; $\chi \circ L$ is a character of $\mathcal{P}(B)$, hence of the form $g \to g(y_0)$ where $y_0 \in B$; let $x_0 \in X_1$ be such that $S(x_0) = y_0$; it is easy to see that $\chi(f) = f(x_0)$ for any $f \in \mathcal{H}(X_1)$.

b) *General case*

Let U be a relatively compact open neighbourhood of X; its boundary δU is compact and disjoint from X; hence for all $y \in \delta U$ there is a function f_y holomorphic on R such that

$$|f_y(y)| > 2$$

and

$$|f_y(x)| \leqq 1 \quad \text{for all} \quad x \in X;$$

there is an open neighbourhood V_y of y on which $|f_y|$ is > 2; let $y_1, \ldots, y_k$ be such that $V_{y_1}, \ldots, V_{y_k}$ cover δU; for $1 \leqq r \leqq 2$, the set X'_r of the points x satisfying $|f_{y_i}(x)| \leqq r$ is disjoint from δU, hence $X_r = X'_r \cap U$ is compact; X_1 satisfies the conditions of a), hence any character of $\mathcal{H}(X_1)$ is of the form $g \to g(y_0)$ where $y_0 \in X_1$.

Further X is the set of points of X_1 satisfying conditions

$$|h_i(x)| \leqq k_i \;\; i \in I \quad \text{and} \quad h_i \in \mathcal{H}(X_1);$$

then let χ be a character of $\mathscr{H}(X)$; combining it with the canonical mapping: $\mathscr{H}(X_1) \to \mathscr{H}(X)$ we obtain a character of $\mathscr{H}(X_1)$, which is of the form $g \to g(y_0)$ where $y_0 \in X_1$; since for all $i \in I$ we have

$$|\chi(h_i \mid X)| = |h_i(y_0)| \leqq \sup_{x \in X} |h_i(x)|$$

y_0 belongs to X; finally it is easy to see that $\chi(f) = f(y_0)$ for all $f \in \mathscr{H}(X)$.

Corollary 2.2. We suppose that R satisfies the axiom (iv) of Stein manifolds (cf. Appendix II, § 2); then for any compact subset X of R and any character χ of $\mathscr{H}(X)$ there is a point x_0 of X' such that $\chi(f \mid X) = f(x_0)$ for any function f holomorphic on R.

Indeed, the mapping $f \mid X' \to f \mid X$ is isometric and hence extends into an isomorphism of $\mathscr{H}(X')$ onto $\mathscr{H}(X)$.

Corollary 2.3. If R is a Stein manifold, for any compact subset X of R there is a homeomorphism from X' onto $\widehat{\mathscr{H}(X)}$ which transforms an arbitrary point x_0 of X' into the character of $\mathscr{H}(X)$ defined by $\chi(f \mid X) = f(x_0)$ for any function f holomorphic on R.

§ 2.4. *The algebra* $\mathscr{O}(R)$

For any complex analytic manifold R which is a countable union of compact subsets we denote by $\mathscr{O}(R)$ the algebra of the functions holomorphic on R endowed with the topology of compact convergence; it is a *Fréchet space.*

Theorem 2.4. If R is a Stein manifold, the canonical mapping from R into $\widehat{\mathscr{O}(R)}$ is a homeomorphism.

This mapping is continuous and injective (cf. § 1.6); it is bijective because if χ is a character of $\mathscr{O}(R)$ it is continuous for one of the semi-norms $\| \ \|_K$, hence proceeds from a character of $\mathscr{H}(K)$, which is defined by a point of R according to the corollary 2.3. Finally it is bicontinuous since the topology of R is the least fine one for which the functions of $\mathscr{O}(R)$ are continuous (cf. Appendix II, § 2).

Proposition 2.1. (Converse of the previous theorem). If the canonical mapping from R into $\widehat{\mathscr{O}(R)}$ is a homeomorphism, R is a Stein manifold.

Since the axiom (iii) for Stein manifolds follows from the other three, it suffices to verify (ii) and (iv); now (ii) holds since the canonical mapping in question, T, is injective; to verify (iv), let us take a compact subset K of R, denoting by K' its holomorphic convex hull and by S the continuous mapping $\widehat{\mathcal{H}(K)} \to \widehat{\mathcal{O}(R)}$, transpose of the restriction mapping $\mathcal{O}(R) \to \mathcal{H}(K)$; Im S is compact; we see readily that $T(K') = \text{Im } S$; hence K', homeomorphic to $T(K')$, is compact.

Theorem 2.5. If R is a spread manifold, $\widehat{\mathcal{O}(R)}$ is homeomorphic to the holomorphy envelope $\tilde{R}$ of R, the character $f \to \tilde{f}(x)$ corresponding to each point x of $\tilde{R}$. (For the definition of holomorphy envelopes see Appendix II, § 3).

Indeed, the mapping $f \to \tilde{f}$ is a topological isomorphism from $\mathcal{O}(R)$ onto $\mathcal{O}(\tilde{R})$, and on the other hand $\tilde{R}$ is a Stein manifold; it suffices therefore to apply the preceding theorem to $\tilde{R}$.

Corollary 2.4. For a spread Stein manifold R, the canonical mapping v from R into $\tilde{R}$ is bijective.

Corollary 2.5. Let R and R' be two spread manifolds, u a holomorphic mapping from R into R'; there is a holomorphic mapping $\tilde{u}$ from $\tilde{R}$ into $\tilde{R}'$ such that $\tilde{u} \circ v = v' \circ u$.

$\tilde{u}$ is merely the "bitranspose" of u.

Remark 2.3. Any value assumed by $\tilde{f}$ is assumed by f; indeed it is the value at f of a character χ of $\mathcal{O}(R)$, and $f - \chi(f)$ cannot be invertible in $\mathcal{O}(R)$.

2.5. *The Spectrum of $\mathcal{O}(R)$: another method*

We will give here another construction for $\widehat{\mathcal{O}(R)}$, assuming the concept of holomorphy envelope is not known.

Theorem 2.5′. Let R be a connected manifold, countable union of compact subsets, and spread in $\mathfrak{C}^n$ by a mapping $u = (u_1, \ldots, u_n)$; there exists on $\widehat{\mathcal{O}(R)}$ a Stein manifold structure with the following properties:

(i) $\widehat{\mathcal{O}(R)}$ is spread in $\mathfrak{C}^n$ by the mapping $\hat{u}$ where $\hat{u}(\chi) = (\chi(u_1), \ldots, \chi(u_n))$;

(ii) the canonical mapping from R into $\widehat{\mathcal{O}(R)}$ is a local isomorphism at each point;

(iii) the Gelfand transformation $f \to \hat{f}$ is a topological isomorphism from $\mathcal{O}(R)$ onto $\mathcal{O}(\widehat{\mathcal{O}(R)})$;

(iv) the underlying topology of the manifold structure of $\widehat{\mathcal{O}(R)}$ is identical to the weak spectrum topology.

Proof

1) *Notations*

For all $k = (k_1, \ldots, k_n) \in \mathfrak{N}^n$ we set

$$|k| = k_1 + \cdots k_n$$

$$k! = k_1! \ldots k_n!;$$

we denote by D_k the differential operator $\delta^k/\delta u_i^{k_1} \ldots \delta u_n^{k_n}$ in $\mathcal{O}(R)$; for any point $z = (z_1, \ldots, z_n)$ of $\mathfrak{C}^n$ we set

$$|z| = \sup |z_i|$$

$$z^k = z_1^{k_1} \ldots z_n^{k_n};$$

we denote by $B(z, r)$ the open polydisc with centre z and radius r, i.e. the set of z' satisfying $|z' - z| < r$. An open subset U of R will be called a *polydisc with center x and radius r* if $u \mid U$ is an isomorphism of U onto an open polydisc in $\mathfrak{C}^n$, with center $u(x)$ and radius r; U will then be denoted $\mathcal{B}(x, r)$. For any point x of R we denote by $d(x)$ the upper bound (strictly positive) of the radii of the polydiscs with center x; the function d is continuous; for any compact subset K of R we denote by $d(K)$ the lower bound (strictly positive) of the $d(x)$ for $x \in K$; for any $a < d(K)$ we set

$$K_a = \bigcup_{x \in K} \overline{B(x, a)};$$

K_a is *compact* as image of $K \times \overline{B(0, a)}$ under the continuous mapping $(x, z) \to u_x^{-1}(u(x) + z)$ where u_x denotes $u \mid \mathcal{B}(x, a')$ with $a < a' < d(K)$.

Finally, for any compact subset K of R we denote by $\sigma(K)$ the set of $\chi \in \widehat{\mathcal{O}(R)}$ such that $\chi(f) \leqq \|f\|_K$ for all $f \in \mathcal{O}(R)$; we recall that the sets $\sigma(K)$ are compact in $\widehat{\mathcal{O}(R)}$ and cover it (cf. Proposition 1.4.).

2) *Construction of local sections L_χ for $\hat{u}$.*

Let χ be a character of $\mathcal{O}(R)$, K a compact subset of R such that $\chi \in \sigma(K)$ and $a < d(K)$; let $f \in \mathcal{O}(R)$ and $k \in \mathfrak{N}^n$; for $x \in K$ we have (Cauchy inequality):

$$|D_k f(x)| \leqq k!\,(2\pi)^{-n} \cdot \|f\|_{\overline{\mathscr{B}(x,a)}} \cdot a^{-|k|}$$

hence

$$|\chi(D_k f)| \leqq \|D_k f\|_K \leqq k!\,(2\pi)^{-n} \cdot \|f\|_{K_a} \cdot a^{-|k|}$$

whence it follows that for $z \in B(\hat{u}(\chi), a)$ the expression

$$\sum_{k \in \mathfrak{N}^n} 1/k! \cdot (z - \hat{u}(\chi))^k \cdot \chi(D_k f)$$

is meaningful and is a continuous linear form with respect to $f \in \mathcal{O}(R)$; it is then easy to see, using Leibnitz' formula, that this form is in fact a character; we will denote it by $L_\chi(x)$ and we have hence by definition

$$(L_\chi(z))\,(f) = \sum_{k \in \mathfrak{N}^n} 1/k! \cdot (z - \hat{u}(\chi))^k \cdot \chi(D_k f);$$

for any $f \in \mathcal{O}(R)$ the function $z \to (L_\chi(z))(f)$ is continuous (and even holomorphic) in $B(\hat{u}(\chi), a)$, hence L_χ is a *continuous* mapping of this polydisc into $\widehat{\mathcal{O}(R)}$; we can immediately verify that

$$\hat{u} \circ L_\chi = \text{identity}$$

and that

$$L_\chi(\hat{u}(\chi)) = \chi.$$

3) *Definition of a manifold structure on $\widehat{\mathcal{O}(R)}$.*

Each L_χ allows us to define on Im L_χ a manifold structure isomorphic to $B(\hat{u}(\chi), a)$; to deduce from it a manifold structure on $\widehat{\mathcal{O}(R)}$ by "patching up", we must prove that on each intersection Im L_χ $\cap$ Im L_χ' the two topologies coincide – – – and this follows from the readily verified fact that if $\chi' \in$ Im L_χ, we have $L_\chi = L_\chi'$ in the neighbourhood of $\hat{u}(\chi')$. We will denote by R' the manifold obtained in this way; it is clear that R' is *spread in $\mathfrak{C}^n$ by u*; we will note that the underlying topology of this manifold structure is finer than the weak spectrum topology, since the L_χ are continuous.

The canonical mapping T of R into R' is an *isomorphism locally at each point*; because if $x \in R$ and if $\chi = T(x)$, we have $u(x) = \hat{u}(\chi)$ and on a suitable neighbourhood of x, T is composed of u and of L_χ; we see in particular that T is *continuous* for the manifold topology of R'.

4) Let us denote by R'' the connected (open and closed) component of $T(R)$ in R'; the mapping $M : f \to \hat{f} \mid R''$ is a *topological isomorphism* of $\mathcal{O}(R)$ onto $\mathcal{O}(R'')$.

First, if $f \in \mathcal{O}(R)$ we have $\hat{f} \in \mathcal{O}(R')$ because all the functions $\hat{f} \circ L_\chi$ are holomorphic by virtue of

$$(\hat{f} \circ L_\chi)(z) = \hat{f}(L_\chi(z)) = (L_\chi(z))(f);$$

then M is

- trivially injective;
- surjective: let $g \in \mathcal{O}(R'')$; we have $g \circ T \in \mathcal{O}(R)$ and there remains to see that $\widehat{g \circ T} = g$, or again that these two functions coincide on Im T - - - which is trivial;
- continuous: because the mapping $f \to \hat{f}$ is continuous when we endow $\mathscr{C}(\widehat{\mathcal{O}(R)})$ with the topology of uniform convergence on the weak compact subsets (cf. Proposition 1.1), and a fortiori if we take the topology of the manifold R'.
- bicontinuous since the inverse mapping is merely $g \to g \circ T$.

5) R'' is a *Stein manifold.*

There remains to verify the axioms (i) and (iv); as regards the latter it suffices according to [13] to show that for any compact subset K of R'' we have

$$d_{R''}(K) = d_{R''}(K')$$

where K' denotes the holomorphic convex hull of K and where $d_{R''}(K)$ and $d_{R''}(K')$ are calculated in R''; to do this, one first shows that if K is a compact subset of R one haves

$$d_{R''}(T(K')) = d_{R'}(\sigma(K) \cap T(R)) \geqq d_{R'}(\sigma(K)) = d_R(K);$$

then one applies this result to a compact subset K of R'' noting that $(R'')''$ is identical to R''.

Finally we verify the axiom (i): R is the union of an increasing sequence of compact subsets K_n, hence R'' is the union of the sets $R'' \cap \sigma(K_n)$, which are compact since R'' is closed in R' and $\sigma(K_n) = (T(K_n))'$.

6) *We have $R'' = R'$ and the two topologies of R' are identical.*

Indeed there exists (Theorem 2.4.) a homeomorphism from R'' onto $\widehat{\mathcal{O}(R'')}$ transforming any point x of R'' into the character $g \to g(x)$; and on the other hand a homeomorphism from $\widehat{\mathcal{O}(R'')}$ onto $\widehat{\mathcal{O}(R)}$ transforming any character χ of $\mathcal{O}(R'')$ into the character $\chi \circ M$ of $\mathcal{O}(R)$; the composite of these two mappings is merely the canonical injection from R'' into $\widehat{\mathcal{O}(R)}$, which is hence a homeomorphism.

Remark 2.4. It is easy to see that the manifold $\widehat{\mathcal{O}(R)}$ is the holomorphy envelope of R defined in Appendix II, § 3, the mappings T and $\hat{u}$ playing here the roles of v and $\tilde{u}$.

§ 2.6. *Return to the algebra $\mathcal{H}(X)$*

Theorem 2.6. Let R be a spread manifold, countable union of compact sets, and X a compact subset of R; $\widehat{\mathcal{H}(X)}$ is homeomorphic to the holomorphic convex hull of $v(X)$ in $\tilde{R}$, to each point y of this hull there corresponding a character χ of $\mathcal{H}(X)$ characterized by $\chi(f \mid X) = \tilde{f}(y)$ $\forall f \in \mathcal{O}(R)$. ($v$ denotes the canonical mapping of R into $\tilde{R}$.)

Indeed the mapping $f \mid X \to \tilde{f} \mid v(X)$ extends into an isometric isomorphism of $\mathcal{H}(X)$ onto $\mathcal{H}(v(X))$.

Corollary 2.6. If X is holomorphically convex in R, so is $v(X)$ in $\tilde{R}$.

Because, let y be a point of the holomorphic convex hull of $v(X)$ and χ the character of $\mathcal{H}(X)$ which corresponds to it; by Theorem 2.3. there exists an $x \in X$ such that $\chi(f) = f(x)$ for any $f \in \mathcal{H}(X)$; we have then for all $g \in \mathcal{O}(\tilde{R})$

$$\chi(g \circ v \mid X) = g(y) = g(v(x))$$

hence $y = v(x) \in v(X)$.

§ 2.7. *The algebra $\mathcal{O}(X)$*

X denotes a compact subset of a spread manifold R, countable union of compact subsets; the algebra $\mathcal{O}(X)$ is defined exactly as in § 1.2, example (c), and has the same properties. X admits a fundamental system of open neighbourhoods which are countable unions of compact subsets; if U and V are two such neighbourhoods satisfying $U \subset V$, the canonical injection of U into V defines by Corollary 2.5 a continuous mapping from $\tilde{U}$ into $\tilde{V}$ it it can readily be verified that the $\tilde{U}$ form thus a projective system of topological spaces; we then deduce the following theorem from Proposition 1.3:

Theorem 2.7. The spectrum of $\mathcal{O}(X)$ is homeomorphic to the projective limit of the holomorphy envelopes of the open neighbourhoods of X which are countable unions of compact subsets.

We note that $\widehat{\mathcal{O}(X)}$ is compact since $\mathcal{O}(X)$ has continuous inverse; on the other hand, the mapping from X into $\widehat{\mathcal{O}(X)}$, projective limit of the mappings $X \to U \to \tilde{U}$ is merely the canonical mapping T.

Remark 2.5. We can prove otherwise that $\varprojlim \tilde{U}$ is compact: for U and V relatively compact open neighbourhoods of X such that $\overline{U} \subset V$, we denote by q the canonical injection from U into V and by $\tilde{q}$ the corresponding holomorphic mapping from $\tilde{U}$ into $\tilde{V}$; we have the following commutative diagram

$$\begin{array}{ccc} U & \xrightarrow{q} & V \\ v_U \downarrow & & \downarrow v_V \\ \tilde{U} & \xrightarrow{\tilde{q}} & \tilde{V} \end{array}$$

it suffices to prove that $\operatorname{Im} \tilde{q}$ is relatively compact; now $\operatorname{Im} (\tilde{q} \circ v_U) = \operatorname{Im} (v_V \circ q)$ is relatively compact and it suffices to prove that $\operatorname{Im} \tilde{q}$ is contained in the holomorphic convex hull of $\operatorname{Im} (\tilde{q} \circ v_U)$, that is to say that for any $f \in \mathcal{O}(\tilde{V})$ and any $x = \tilde{q}(y)$ with $y \in \tilde{U}$, we have

$$|f(x)| \leq \sup |f(z)| \quad \text{for} \quad z \in \operatorname{Im} (\tilde{q} \circ v_U);$$

now the number $f(x) = (f \circ \tilde{q})(y)$ is a value assumed by the function $f \circ \tilde{q} \circ v_U$ according to Remark 2.3.

Corollary 2.7. If X admits a fundamental system of open neighbourhoods which are Stein manifolds, the canonical mapping from X into $\widehat{\mathcal{O}(X)}$ is a homeomorphism.

Proposition 2.2. (Cartan's theorem on the zeros). Let X be a compact subset of a manifold R such that $\widehat{\mathcal{O}(X)} = X$; let $f_1, \ldots, f_p$ be elements of $\mathcal{O}(X)$ without common zero in X; there exist elements $g_1, \ldots, g_p$ of $\mathcal{O}(X)$ such that $\sum f_i g_i = 1$ in the sense of $\mathcal{O}(X)$.

Indeed, the f_i are contained in no maximal ideal, since such an ideal is always the kernel of a character (cf. Proposition 1.6.); they therefore generate the unit ideal.

This will occur in particular if $R = \mathfrak{C}^n$ and if X is rationally convex (see Corollary 2.9).

§ 2.8. *The Banach algebra* $\mathcal{H}_1(X)$

X denotes a compact subset of a manifold R, a countable union of compact subsets; $\mathcal{H}_1(X)$ is the inductive limit in the sense of the category of the Banach algebras of the algebras $H^\infty(U)$, U an open neighbourhood of X (cf. Remark 1.5); on the other hand, $\mathcal{O}(X)$ is the inductive limit of the same algebras in the sense of the category of the category of the locally convex algebras (cf. § 1.2, example (c)); we have thus

Theorem 2.8. $\widehat{\mathcal{H}_1(X)}$ is homeomorphic to $\widehat{\mathcal{O}(X)}$; more precisely if we denote by M the canonical mapping from $\mathcal{O}(X)$ into $\mathcal{H}_1(X)$, the mapping ${}^tM$ from $\widehat{\mathcal{H}_1(X)}$ into $\widehat{\mathcal{O}(X)}$ is homeomorphic.

Corollary 2.8. If R is spread and if X admits a fundamental system of open neighbourhoods which are Stein manifolds, the canonical mapping from X into $\widehat{\mathcal{H}_1(X)}$ is a homeomorphism; in particular this is always true if R is a Riemann surface.

Corollary 2.9. If X is a rationally convex compact subset of $\mathfrak{C}^n$, the canonical mappings from X into $\widehat{\mathcal{O}(X)}$ and into $\mathcal{H}_1(X)$ are homeomorphismus.

Follows from Remark 2.2.

Theorem 2.9. Let R be a Stein manifold and X a holomorphically convex compact subset of R; then $\mathcal{H}(X) = \mathcal{H}_1(X)$.

Sketch of the proof (moore details are given in [6], Theorem 10.5.)

The problem is to prove that for any function f holomorphic on a relatively compact open neighbourhood U of X, we have $f \mid X \in \mathcal{H}(X)$; now it can be proved ([7]) that there exists a holomorphic mapping

u from R into a space $\mathfrak{C}^n$ such that $u \mid U$ is an isomorphism from U onto an analytic subset of an open set of $\mathfrak{C}^n$; we denote $u = (u_1, \ldots, u_n)$; $f \circ u^{-1}$ is a holomorphic function on $u(U)$; since the characters of $\mathcal{H}(X)$ are exactly the mappings $g \to g(x)$ where $x \in X$, we have

$$sp\ (u_1 \mid X, \ldots u_n \mid X) = u(X);$$

$f \circ u^{-1}$ is hence holomorphic on an analytic subset containing this simultaneous spectrum; by virtue of an improvement of the functional calculus described in [8], Chapter IV, there exists an element g of $\mathcal{H}(X)$ such that

$$g = f \circ u^{-1} \circ (\widehat{u_1 \mid X}, \ldots \widehat{u_n \mid X})$$

that is to say that $g(x) = f(x)$ for all $x \in X$ or finally that $f \mid X \in \mathcal{H}(X)$.

Corollary 2.10. Under the same hypotheses, the canonical mappings from X into $\widehat{\mathcal{H}_1(X)}$ and into $\mathcal{O}(X)$ are homeomorphisms.

Because this is true for $\mathcal{H}(X)$ (cf. Corollary 2.3).

APPENDIX I

INDUCTIVE AND PROJECTIVE LIMITS

§ 1. *Case of sets*

An *inductive system of sets* consits in the giving

(i) of a set of indices I, ordered and filtering to the right

(ii) of a family $(E_i)_{i \in I}$ of sets

(iii) for any pair of indices (i, j) satisfying $i \leqq j$, of a mapping $P_{i,j} : E_i \to E_j$, in such a way that for any triplet of indices (i, j, k) satisfying $i \leqq j \leqq k$ we have $P_{i,k} = P_{j,k} \circ P_{i,j}$ and that for all i, $P_{i,i}$ is the identity mapping.

The *inductive limit* set, denoted by $\varinjlim E_i$, is the quotient of the sum set of the E_i by the following equivalence relation R: let $x \in E_i$ and $y \in E_j$; then $R(x, y)$ if and only if there is an index $k \geqq i, j$ such that $P_{i,k}(x) = P_{j,k}(y)$. We will denote by P_i the canonical mapping from E_i into $\varinjlim E_i$; we note that we have $\varinjlim E_i = \bigcup_i \operatorname{Im} P_i$.

Let F be a set; a family of mappings $T_i : E_i \to F$ is an *inductive system of mappings* if for any pair (i, j) satisfying $i \leqq j$ we have $T_j \circ P_{i,j} = T_i$; there exists then one and only one mapping T from $\varinjlim E_i$ into F satisfying $T \circ P_i = T_i$ for all i; we often write $T = \varinjlim T_i$.

The concept of projective limit is rather similar to that of inductive limit (it is, precisely, the "dual" concept); to obtain the definition of a *projective system of sets* it suffices to replace $E_i \to E_j$ by $E_j \to E_i$ and $P_{i,k} = P_{j,k} \circ P_{i,j}$ by $P_{i,k} = P_{i,j} \circ P_{j,k}$.

The *projective limit* set, denoted $\varprojlim E_i$, is the subset of the product set of the E_i composed of the families (x_i) satisfying $x_i = P_{i,j}(x_j)$ for any pair $i \leqq j$; we denote by P_i the canonical mapping from $\varprojlim E_i$ into E_i.

Let F be a set; a family of mappings $T_i : F \to E_i$ is a *projective system of a mappings* if for any pair $i \leqq j$ we have $P_{i,j} \circ T_j = T_i$; there exists then one and only one mapping $T : F \to \varprojlim E_i$ satisfying $P_i \circ T = T_i$ for all i; if $y \in F$ $T(y)$ is merely the family $(T_i(y))$; one often writes $T = \varprojlim T_i$.

§ 2. *Case of topological spaces*

To define the inductive and projective limits of topological spaces we require moreover that the mappings $P_{i,j}$ be continuous. In the case of an inductive system the set $\varinjlim E_i$ is endowed with the finest topology which makes all the P_i continuous; if we have an inductive system (T_i) of continuous mappings from the E_i into a topological space F, the mapping $\varinjlim T_i$ is automatically continuous. In the case of a projective system of topological spaces the set $\varprojlim E_i$ is endowed with the topology induced by the product topology on $\prod E_i$; if we have a projective system (T_i) of continuous mappings from a topological space F into the E_i, the mapping $\varprojlim T_i$ is automatically continuous.

§ 3. *Case of (complex) vector spaces*

To define the inductive or projective systems of vector spaces, we require that the mappings $P_{i,j}$ be linear. In the case of an inductive system the set $\varinjlim E_i$ is endowed with a vector space structure which can be described in the following manner: let x and $y \in \varinjlim E_i$; there is an index k and there are elements x_k and y_k of E_k such that $x = P_k(x_k)$ and $y = P_k(y_k)$; we set $x + y = P_k(x_k + y_k)$ and for every scalar $a : ax = P_k(ax_k)$; the result does not depend on the choice of k, x_k and y_k. If we have an inductive system (T_i) of linear mappings from the E_i into a vector space F the mapping $\varinjlim T_i$ is automatically linear.

In the case of a projective system, the set $\varprojlim E_i$ is endowed with a vector space structure obtained by considering it as a subspace of the space $\prod E_i$; if we have a projective system of linear mappings from a vector space F into the E_i, the mapping $\varprojlim T_i$ is automatically linear.

§ 4. *Case of locally convex topological vector spaces* (LCTVS)

To define the inductive or projective systems of LCTVS's it is clear that we will assume the mappings $P_{i,j}$ are linear and continuous. In the case of an inductive limit, the vector space $\varinjlim E_i$ is endowed with the finest *locally convex* topology which makes all the linear mappings $P_{i,j}$ continuous, topology which can be described in the following manner: a balanced convex subset B of $\varinjlim E_i$ is a neighbourhood of 0 in $\varinjlim E_i$ if and only if each $P_i^{-1}(B)$ is a neighbourhood of 0 in E_i; if we have an inductive system (T_i) of continuous linear mappings from the E_i into a LCTVS F, the mapping $\varinjlim T_i$ is automatically linear and continuous.

In the case of a projective system, the set $\varprojlim E_i$ is endowed with the (LCTVS) structure of topological vector subspace of $\prod E_i$; it is clear that if (T_i) is a projective system of continuous linear mappings from a LCTVS F into the E_i the mapping $\varprojlim T_i$ is automatically linear and continuous.

We will use the following results:

– if f is a continuous linear form on $\varprojlim E_i$, there exist an index i and a continuous linear form g on E_i such that $f = g \circ P_i$ (cf. [10] § 22.6);

– let E be a LCTVS whose topology is defined by a filtering family $(p_i)_{i \in I}$ of semi-norms; for all i we denote by E_i the completed Banach space of E for the semi-norm P_i and by T_i the canonical mapping from E into E_i; for any pair $i \leqq j$ let $P_{i,j}$ be the mapping from the E_j into E_i extending T_i; then the E_i form a projective system and the mapping $\varprojlim T_i$ is a topological isomorphism from E onto an everywhere dense vector subspace of $\varprojlim E_i$ (cf. [10], § 19.9).

Remark 1. We see that in each of the studied cases – – – in each category studied: sets, topological spaces, vector spaces, LCTVS – – – the object $\varprojlim E_i$ is a "subobject" of a "direct-product object"; we could verify without difficulty that the object $\varinjlim E_i$ is a "quotient object" of a "direct-sum object"; but for the last three cases we preferred another description of $\varinjlim E_i$. On the other hand the inductive and projective limits are solutions of universal problems in each of the categories we considered.

Remark 2. It is easy to see that in each of the four cases considered, the inductive limit and the projective limit do not change when we replace the set of indices I by a cofinal subset, that is such that each element of I is majorized by an element of this subset; this remark will often be very useful.

APPENDIX II
COMPLEX ANALYTIC MANIFOLDS

§ 1. *Definition of complex analytic manifolds*

Grosso modo, a complex analytic manifold is a topological space R for which we distinguish certain complex-valued functions, called holomorphic functions, in such a way that it is locally "the same thing" as a space $\mathfrak{C}^n$ with the usual holomorphic functions; but the functions in question can be defined on arbitrary open subsets of R, and not necessarily on the whole of R.

More precisely, a *complex analytic manifold* consists in the giving of a separated topological space R, and, for any open subset U of R, of a ring $\mathcal{O}(U)$ of functions continuous on U so that the following conditions are satisfied:

(i) the constant functions belong to $\mathcal{O}(U)$

(ii) if we have two open subsets $V \subset U$ and if $f \in \mathcal{O}(U)$, then $f \mid V \in \mathcal{O}(V)$

(iii) If $U = \bigcup_i U_i$, if $f_i \in \mathcal{O}(U_i)$ for all i and if $f_i \mid U_i \cap U_j = f_j \mid U_i \cap U_j$ for all i and all j, then the function f on U defined by $f \mid U_i = f_i$ for all i belongs to $\mathcal{O}(U)$

(iv) for any point x of R there exist an open neighbourhood U of x, an open neighbourhood V of 0 in a space $\mathfrak{C}^n$ and a homeomorphism P from U onto V transforming $\mathcal{O}(U)$ into the set of functions holomorphic on V.

The number n is called *dimension of R in x*. If we use the language of sheaves, we can say that we have a subsheaf of the sheaf of functions continuous on R.

For any open subset U of R, the elements of $\mathcal{O}(U)$ are called *holomorphic functions on U*; for any points x of R the elements of the set $\mathcal{O}_x$, inductive limit of the $\mathcal{O}(U)$ when U runs over the set of open neighbourhoods of x, are called *germs of holomorphic functions* at x; for instance, if $R = \mathfrak{C}$ such a germ is merely a power series with non-zero radius of convergence.

The homeomorphism P of condition (iv) is called *local map* at x; by combining it with the coordinate functions $z \to z_1, \ldots, z_n$, we obtain a *system of local coordinates* at x.

A continuous mapping from a manifold R into a manifold R' is said to be *holomorphic* if for any function f' holomorphic on an open set U' of R', $f' \circ u$ is holomorphic on $u^{-1}(U')$; moreover we say that u is a *local isomorphism* at a point x of R is x admits an open neighbourhod U such that $u \mid U$ be a homeomorphism from U onto an open subset $U' = u(U)$ of R'; the inverse mapping from U' onto U is then holomorphic.

Let R be a manifold; a closed subset E of R is said to be *analytic* if any point of E admits an open neighbourhood V such that $E \cap V$ is the set of common zeros of a finite family of holomorphic functions on V; we note in passing that if R is an open polydisc of $\mathfrak{C}^n$, this implies that E is the set of common zeros of a family of holomorphic functions on R; a function f on a open subset U of E is said to be *holomorphic* at a point x of U if it is the restriction to U of a function holomorphic on a neighbourhood of x in R.

A manifold R is said to be *spread* ("in $\mathfrak{C}^n$" is understood) if there is a holomorphic mapping u from R into $\mathfrak{C}^n$ which is a local isomorphism at each point; in other words; if there exist holomorphic functions on $R: u_1, \ldots, u_n$, forming at each point a system of local coordinates.

Examples

1) Any open subset of a space $\mathfrak{C}^n$ is a spread manifold.

2) A compact manifold is never spread, because any function holomorphic on such a manifold is constant.

3) The manifolds of dimension 1 are called *Riemann surfaces*.

§ 2. *Stein manifolds*

We call thus any manifold R satisfying the following axioms:

(i) R is a countable union of compact subsets

(ii) $\mathcal{O}(R)$ separates the points of R

(iii) for any point x of R there exist functions $f_1, \ldots, f_n \in \mathcal{O}(R)$ forming a system of local coordinates at x

(iv) for any compact subset K of R the set K' of the y satisfying

$$|f(y)| \leq \sup_{x \in K} |f(x)| \quad \text{for all} \quad f \in \mathcal{O}(R)$$

– – – called *holomorphic convex hull* of K – – – is compact.

In fact one can prove that the axiom (iii) follows from the three others (Grauert).

Examples

1) Any space $\mathfrak{C}^n$ is a Stein manifold; here the concept of holomorphic convex hull is identical to that of polynomial convex hull.

2) Any open subset U of $\mathfrak{C}$ is a Stein manifold; the only non-obvious axioms is (iv); let thus K' be the holomorphic convex hull of a compact subset K of U; for any point y of the boundary δU of U the function $z \to 1/(z - y)$ is holomorphic on U; hence K' is contained in the set E of the points z of $\mathfrak{C}$ satisfying

$$1/|z - y| \leq \sup_{x \in K} 1/|x - y|$$

i.e.

$$|z - y| \geq d(y, K) \quad \text{for all} \quad y \in \delta U;$$

K' is then contained in the set E_1 of the points z of $\mathfrak{C}$ satisfying the above condition as well as

$$|z| \leq \sup_{x \in K} |x|;$$

where E_1 is compact and disjoint from δU, $E_1 \cap U$ is compact; finally K' is closed in U and contained in $E_1 \cap U$, hence compact.

3) On the other hand an open subset of $\mathfrak{C}^n$ $(n > 1)$ does not necessarily verify the axiom (iv); let us take for instance $n = 2$, the points of $\mathfrak{C}^2$ being denoted by $z = (z_1, z_2)$; we define U by the conditions

$$|z_1| < 1, |z_2| < 1, z_1 \text{ or } z_2 \neq 0$$

and K by the conditions

$$|z_1| \leq \tfrac{1}{2}, |z_2| \leq \tfrac{1}{2}, |z_1| \text{ or } |z_2| = \tfrac{1}{2};$$

if f is holomorphic on U and if $|z_2| \leqq \frac{1}{2}$, we have, by virtue of the maximal principle applied to the function $z_1 \to f(z_1, z_2)$:

$$|f(0, z_2)| \leqq \sup_{z_1 = 1/2} |f(z_1, z_2)| \leqq \sup_{z \in K} |f(z)|;$$

hence all the points $(0, z_2)$ with $|z_2| \leqq \frac{1}{2}$ belong to K', which can hence not be compact.

4) Any open subset U of $\mathfrak{C}^n$ defined by conditions $|f_i(z)| < k_i$, $i = 1, \ldots, p$, f_i polynomials, is a Stein manifold; indeed, let K be a compact subset of U, K' its holomorphic convex hull in U and K'' is polynomial convex (compact) hull in $\mathfrak{C}^n$; we have

$$|f_i(z)| \leqq l_i < k_i \quad (i = 1, \ldots p)$$

for all $z \in K$, hence for all $z \in K''$ and consequently $K'' \subset U$; on the other hand $K' \subset K''$.

5) A compact manifold is never a Stein manifold, since all holomorphic functions on such a manifold are constant.

6) It can be shown that any connected non-compact Riemann surface is a Stein manifold.

Property. We will use the following property of Stein manifolds; it has been shown ([14]) that any connected Stein manifold R is isomorphic to an analytic subset E of a space $\mathfrak{C}^n$; this means that there is a homeomorphism P from R onto E which, for all points x of R, transforms the set of germs of holomorphic functions at x into the set of germs of holomorphic functions at $P(x)$. It follows that the topology of R is the least fine which makes continuous the functions of $\mathcal{O}(R)$; and this obviously remains true if we do not assume R connected.

§ 3. *Envelopes of holomorphy*

It can be shown that if U is an arbitrary open subset of $\mathfrak{C}$ there is a holomorphic function on U which cannot be holomorphically extended to any open subset U' larger than U (at least if we require that any connected component of U' meet U!); however this is no longer true for all open subsets of $\mathfrak{C}^n$ if $n > 1$; for instance it is easy to see that in example 3) of § 2 any holomorphic function on U extends into a function holomorphic on $U \cup \{0\}$; an open subset admitting an inextensible holomorphic function is called a *domain of holomorphy*; it can be proved that this is so if and only if the open set in question is a Stein manifold, i.e. verifies the axiom (iv) of § 2.

In example 3) of § 2, $U \cup \{0\}$ is the largest open subset V containing U and such that any holomorphic function of U extends uniquely into a holomorphic function on V: it is the *holomorphy envelope* of U; we can now ask ourselves if any open set admits an evelope of holomorphy; the answer is negative, but becomes positive if we agree to go out of $\mathfrak{C}^n$ in order to take *spread manifolds*; so to state the main result we can start from arbitrary spread manifolds, and not only from open subsets of $\mathfrak{C}^n$.

Main result. Let R be a manifold, countable union of compact subsets and spread in $\mathfrak{C}^n$ by a mapping u; there exist a manifold $\tilde{R}$, spread by a mapping $\tilde{u}$, and a mapping $v : R \to \tilde{R}$ which is a local isomorphism at each point, with the following properties:

(i) $\tilde{u} \circ v = u$

(ii) for any function f holomorphic on R there exists a function $\tilde{f}$ holomorphic on $\tilde{R}$, and only one such function, satisfying $\tilde{f} \cdot v = f$

(iii) if $\tilde{R}$, $\tilde{u}'$ and v' have the properties analogous to (*i*) and (ii), there exists a holomorphic mapping $w : \tilde{R}' \to \tilde{R}$ such that $w \circ v' = v$, $\tilde{u} \circ w = \tilde{u}'$, $\tilde{f} \circ w = \tilde{f}'$ for all $f \in \mathcal{O}(R)$.

The triplet $(\tilde{R}, \tilde{u}, v)$ is unique in the sense that if $(\tilde{R}_1, \tilde{u}_1, v_1)$ has the properties analogous to (i), (ii), (iii) there exists an isomorphism from $\tilde{R}_1$ onto $\tilde{R}$ with properties analogous to those of the above-mentioned w. $\tilde{R}$ is a Stein manifold; it is then clear that v is injective if and only if $\mathcal{O}(R)$ separates the points of R. The mapping $f \to f \circ v$ is an algebraic isomorphism from $\mathcal{O}(\tilde{R})$ onto $\mathcal{O}(R)$ and it is clear that it is continuous; it is bicontinuous by virtue of the Banach theorem (we recall that $\mathcal{O}(R)$ and $\mathcal{O}(\tilde{R})$ are Fréchet spaces); in other words it is a *topological isomorphism.*